mammals

An **EXPLORE YOUR WORLD**™ Handbook

DISCOVERY COMMUNICATIONS
Founder, Chairman, and Chief Executive Officer:
  John S. Hendricks
President and Chief Operating Officer:
  Judith A. McHale
President, Discovery Enterprises Worldwide:
  Michela English

DISCOVERY CHANNEL PUBLISHING
Vice President, Publishing: Natalie Chapman
Editorial Director: Rita Thievon Mullin
Senior Editor: Mary Kalamaras
Editorial Coordinator: Heather Quinlan

DISCOVERY CHANNEL RETAIL
Product Development: Tracy Fortini
Naturalist: Steve Manning

DISCOVERY COMMUNICATIONS, INC., produces high-quality television programming, interactive media, books, films, and consumer products. DISCOVERY NETWORKS, a division of Discovery Communications, Inc., operates and manages the Discovery Channel, TLC, Animal Planet, the Travel Channel, and the Discovery Health Channel.

Mammals, An Explore Your World ™ Handbook, was created and produced by ST. REMY MEDIA INC.

A CIP catalogue record for this book is available from the British Library.

ISBN   1 84201 010 7

Discovery Channel Online website address:
http://www.discovery.com
Printed in the United States of America on acid-free paper
First Edition   10 9 8 7 6 5 4 3 2 1

CONSULTANTS

Jacques Dancosse has worked as a veterinarian at the Los Angeles Zoo, the Ménagerie du Jardin in Paris, and the Biodome in Montreal, where he is currently involved in field research on beluga whales.

Judith Eger has more than thirty years of experience in mammalian and museum research. She holds a Ph.d. in zoology from the University of Toronto, and is the current senior curator of the Centre for Biodiversity and Conservation Biology at the Royal Ontario Museum. Her interest in mammalian evolution recently took her to Vietnam, where she completed a three-year study of indigenous bats.

Philip Myers is an associate curator of the mammals section of the Museum of Zoology at the University of Michigan, where he has also been teaching since 1982. He has been a research associate at the American Museum of Natural History since 1988. Dr. Myers has published more than thirty articles and manuscripts in the field of mammal research, primarily in the fields of systematics, biogeography, and the natural history of small mammals. He has done extensive field work in South America as well as throughout the United States.

Donna Naughton has been a research assistant in the mammal section of the Canadian Museum of Nature since 1974. Her main interests are mammalian ecology, taxonomy, distribution, and behavior. Past projects include taxonomy of bison, shrews, mice, and bats; identification of mammal hair and scat; and species distribution in Canada.

Fiona Reid is a departmental associate of mammalogy at the Royal Ontario Museum in Toronto, where she focuses her research on neo-tropical bats. She is the author of *A Field Guide to the Mammals of Central America and Southeast Mexico* and has illustrated numerous other books on mammals.

mammals

An **EXPLORE YOUR WORLD**™ Handbook

DISCOVERY BOOKS

LONDON

CONTENTS

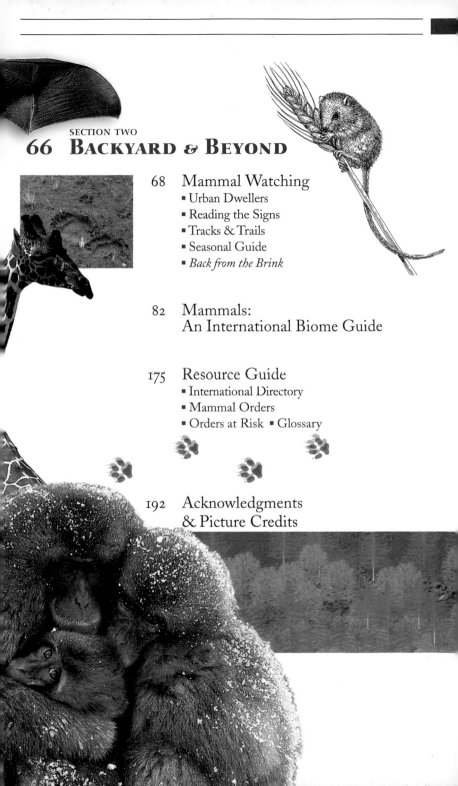

LIVING BY DESIGN

BODY BASICS

Despite their myriad shapes and sizes, all mammals possess some common basic physical similarities.

In the course of the last 200 million years, mammals have evolved to populate countless niches and to embrace a mind-boggling array of shapes and sizes—from the lilliputian Kitti's hog-nosed bat (*Craseonycteris thonglongyai*) that weighs less than one-tenth ounce (3 g) to the leviathan, 120-ton blue whale (*Balaenoptera musculus*). As diverse as they are, however, all mammals share certain fundamental physical characteristics: They are warm-blooded; they have hair or fur over at least some part of their body; most possess large external ears and a mouth full of teeth; and they are usually endowed with modified sweat glands, called mammary glands, which, in the females, produce milk to feed their young.

ANIMALS WITH BACKBONE
Although new species are still being discovered at a rapid rate, the present count stands at 4,629 mammal species. Together, mammals represent one of the five major groups of vertebrates—animals that possess vertebral columns—a group that also includes fish, amphibians, reptiles, and birds.

BARREL-SHAPED RIB CAGE

PELVIS
Provides a surface for the attachment of the powerful muscles that support the heavy, stooped torso.

GLUTEUS MAXIMUS
Undeveloped buttock muscles (compared to man's) keep the gorilla's bipedal motion at a shuffle.

UTERUS
Lacking the horns that distinguish the uteri of many other types of mammals (page 40), this gorilla's uterus contains a single foetus nearing the end of its gestation.

BRAIN
The brain of a gorilla is larger and more highly convoluted relative to less developed mammals (page 44).

TEETH
Sharpened canines and incisors (page 32) act as shearing blades when the gorilla snacks on ground plants.

LUNGS

STOMACH

LARGE INTESTINE

SMALL INTESTINE

Simplified Anatomy of a Female Gorilla
Like most mammals, this female gorilla has four limbs and a strong skull to protect its large brain. As well, its thoracic cavity contains a four-chambered heart and a pair of lungs.

Several of the features that distinguish mammals from other vertebrates only become evident through studying the mammal's basic skeletal structure. For example, unlike other vertebrates, mammals have three middle-ear bones, or ossicles. Derived from bones that were originally part of the lower jaw of mammals' distant ancestors, the ossicles help amplify sound, thus enhancing the animals' hearing (page 48).

Another skeletal difference can be seen in the mammalian dentary, the tooth-bearing part of the lower jaw, which changed considerably as mammals evolved. In keeping with a generalized evolutionary trend toward a reduction in the number of bones in the skull, most of the lower jaw bones became smaller and eventually disappeared. Some, however, became the ossicles of the middle ear, and one, the dentary, grew larger. From taking up only about half of the jaw, the dentary of today's mammals has expanded until it forms a new jaw joint with the skull.

Mammals derive their name from the Latin word Mamma, *meaning "breast." The breasts of most female mammals, including this ring-tailed lemur (Lemur catta), contain mammary glands, united to form a nipple, or teat. The glands begin to manufacture milk when stimulated by hormones during late pregnancy and continue to produce it as long as the young are nursing.*

The teeth of mammals have also undergone significant changes in the course of evolution. Some 290 million years ago, the precursors of modern mammals had teeth that were all the same size and shape. Gradually, as hunting and eating habits diversified (page 32), teeth became more specialized, designed to process food before digestion can occur. The mammalian stomach is usually made of a single saclike organ, although among some mammals, such as ruminant artiodactyls and cetaceans, it is subdivided into chambers.

Other significant mammalian features include a unique muscular wall, or diaphragm, that separates the chest cavity from the

*"You'll see green alligators
and long-necked geese,
Some humpty-backed camels
and some chimpanzees,
Some cats and rats and elephants,
but sure as you're born,
You're never gonna see no unicorn."*

— SHEL SILVERSTEIN

abdominal cavity; a well-developed brain; and a four-chambered heart that receives venous blood from the body in the right side, which it then pumps to the lungs, and oxygenated blood from the lungs in the left side, which it then pumps to the body. The rate at which the heart pumps blood varies from species to species: Many small mammals, such as shrews and chipmunks, have heart rates that exceed five hundred beats a minute, whereas the rates of large mammals tend to be much lower—the heart rate of the Asian elephant (*Elephas maximus*), for instance, typically measures between twenty five and fifty beats a minute.

IN WARM BLOOD

The ability of mammals to adapt to the extreme environments of Earth is largely due to their warm-bloodedness—that is, their ability to maintain a stable, or nearly stable, active body temperature of about from 107 to 86 degrees Fahrenheit (42 to 30°C). Birds also possess this ability, but fish, amphibians, and reptiles do not; these vertebrates rely on a variety of external sources of heat to keep warm, and so are described as cold-blooded, or ectothermic.

Although fossil evidence reveals nothing about how or when early mammals became warm-blooded, or endothermic, the mechanism of staying warm is clear. A high metabolic rate (for smaller mammals this can measure eight times that of reptiles) allows mammals to burn fat reserves in their body and to generate heat in their muscles and other tissues. This enables them to function when it's cold.

Warm-bloodedness has helped mammals not only to adapt to extreme environments, but also to become nocturnal, and thus avoid becoming prey for some of the larger diurnal reptiles. The ability to hunt and forage during the colder night also diminished competition with reptiles for the same food sources.

Hair of the Sloth

Many mammals have hair that is colored to help them blend into their natural settings. The sloths of Central and South America put their own special twist on the art of camouflage: They have large, coarse tufts of vertically and horizontally serrated hairs that collect airborne green algae produced by their humid rain-forest habitat. The algae gives the sloth's gray or brown hairs a green tinge that makes it difficult for predators to spot the sloths as they hang in the trees.

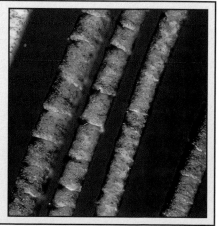

High Cost of Living

Scientists use mathematical formulas to calculate the high energy costs of maintaining the metabolic rate needed by mammals to stay warm. The budget is made up of the energy the mammal consumes, the energy it conserves, and the energy it expends. The terms of the formula are expressed in kilojoules (kj) (one kj = 0.24 calories). Calculations have been done for a variety of mammal species, including the vampire bat (*Desmodus rotundus*), a highly specialized creature that only feeds on blood.

Energy in = energy out +/- biomass change

• "Energy in" refers to the amount of energy taken into the body. In the case of the vampire bat, it refers to the amount of blood the bat drinks in a day less the amount of energy it loses through its excrement.

• "Energy out" refers to the amount of energy the vampire bat's non-flight metabolism expends plus the energy spent while flying (about a half hour per day to get food).

• "Biomass change" refers to the energy profit the bat is left with at the end of the day. It can store this excess energy as body fat, use it to grow, or use it for reproductive purposes. When the bat expends more energy than it is taking in—something an exercising dieter hopes to achieve—the biomass change can be a negative number, hence the +/- symbol in the formula.

Despite its advantages, there is a high cost attached to being warm-blooded. In general, a mammal consumes five to ten times as much energy as a reptile of equal size, and when the temperature drops, it may expend twenty to thirty times as much energy. Mammals, like birds, therefore need plenty of reliable food resources in order to stay alive.

When warm-bloodedness alone is not enough to handle cold temperatures, mammals may take more drastic measures to ensure their survival. Some marine mammals, such as large filter-feeding whales, migrate to warm waters to breed or to wait out the cold. During this time, they live off their body fat.

If migrating to avoid cold weather or an insufficiency of food is not an option, mammals may resort to shallow torpor, a self-induced lowering of the body temperature, or deep torpor, a comatose condition where the body temperature may drop to within 1.5 degrees Fahrenheit (1°C) or less of the ambient temperature. This comatose condition may also include prolonged periods of apnea, where breathing ceases entirely. In the winter, deep torpor is referred to as hibernation, and it is seasonally practiced in northern climates by small mammals, especially rodents and bats. Body size and torpor are related. The bigger the mammal, the more energy that is used up to arouse from a period of dormancy. The largest mammals to enter deep torpor are marmots, which weigh about twenty-two pounds (5 kg) and take hours to arouse. Bears would need a day's energy expenditure to warm up from deep torpor, so instead the black bear (*Ursus americanus*), for instance, spends winter in shallow torpor, its temperature hovering at about eighty-eight degrees Fahrenheit (31°C), only about twelve degrees Fahrenheit (7°C) below its normal level.

Some mammals resort to shallow torpor for only brief periods. For example, rodents such as the California pocket mouse (*Chaetodipus californicus*) that dwell in extreme climates can lower their heart rate for a few hours at a time to conserve energy when food is hard to come by.

The ability of small mammals such as the eastern chipmunk (Tamias striatus) to hibernate greatly extends their geographical range.

COPING WITH THE HEAT

Endothermia serves mammals best when their body temperature is warmer than the air temperature. In hot environments such as deserts, they face greater challenges and require specialized physiological mechanisms to cool down. Some mammals, such as humans and other primates, stay cool by sweating through glands in the skin. Those with few or no sweat glands—among them dogs—pant to evaporate moisture on the tongue and in the nasal chambers. Many desert rodent species retreat into caves or underground burrows and dens by day and emerge only at night. Too big to hide from the sun, camels and other large desert species must tough out heat and a lack of water. Especially when going without water, camels relax their ability to maintain a stable temperature, letting their body climb as high as 104 degrees Fahrenheit (40°C) by day and dive as low as 94 degrees Fahrenheit (34.5°C) at night.

Most mammals grow an insulating coat of hair or fur, usually to help retain body heat, but also, as in the case of the woolly-coated camel, to help protect against excess heat. Hair is made of dead skin cells strengthened by keratin, a tough, horny tissue made of protein. It grows from pits, or follicles, in the skin. The types of hair or coats of fur that are produced depend on the needs of individual species. Some big hot-weather mammals such as rhinoceroses and hippopotamuses are only sparsely covered in hair. Animals from cold northern or alpine climates—mountain goats, yaks, and muskox—usually sport the longest coats. Other species, namely sea lions, otters, and polar bears, need especially thick coats to protect them from frigid ocean waters. These animals usually have an undercoat of short, soft hairs, which traps a layer of air against the skin to prevent cold water from making contact. As well, they have an outer coat of long, stiff hairs, called guard hairs. An oily substance secreted by the sebaceous glands serves as waterproofing.

Mammals occasionally shed their coat and replace it with a new one. Depending on a number of factors, shedding can occur seasonally or at an even pace all year long. Where winters are cold enough to require a thick coat, mammals grow one, then shed it in favor of a lighter coat when warm weather returns.

Some hair serves other functions than warmth. Most mammals grow long, stiff sensory hairs, known as vibrissae, which serve as touch organs *(page 53)*. The protective spines of hedgehogs, echidnas, and tenrecs are akin to hair, as are the barbed quills of porcupines.

To avoid being detected by predator or prey, many mammals have coats similar in color to their physical surroundings. Many plains mammals—lions, for example— have sandy- or tan-colored coats. Other big felines, such as tigers or leopards, have striped or spotted coats that serve to camouflage them as they move about their forest or grassland homes. The arctic fox (*Alopex lagopus*) has a winter coat as white as its snowy northern habitat. In the spring, it turns a light blue or brown, allowing the fox to fade into the grayer, slushier surroundings.

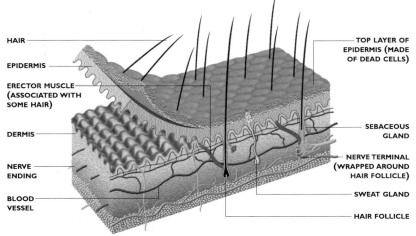

HAIR

EPIDERMIS

ERECTOR MUSCLE (ASSOCIATED WITH SOME HAIR)

DERMIS

NERVE ENDING

BLOOD VESSEL

TOP LAYER OF EPIDERMIS (MADE OF DEAD CELLS)

SEBACEOUS GLAND

NERVE TERMINAL (WRAPPED AROUND HAIR FOLLICLE)

SWEAT GLAND

HAIR FOLLICLE

More Than Skin Deep

A mammal's skin is made up of the epidermis, a thin protective layer that is kept lubricated by glandular secretions from below, and the dermis, a thicker, stronger layer that supports the blood and nerve supply to the epidermis. The dermis contains sweat glands and sebaceous glands, which vary according to their position on the body. In canids, for example, modified sebaceous glands are found around the anus and on the tail, where they exude secretions used in social recognition.

Mammal Classification

To classify all Earth's known plants and animals, scientists have traditionally used a hierarchical system of classification that was based on overall similarity among organisms.

In 1749 Swedish botanist Carolus Linnaeus introduced a binomial nomenclature, giving each plant in his large collection a generic and a specific name. The system was later extended to the animal kingdom.

The system, which was introduced by the eighteenth-century Swedish botanist Carolus Linnaeus, separates animals from plants and places each at the head of its own kingdom. The two kingdoms are broken down into successively smaller, less inclusive groups, including phylums, subphylums, classes, orders, families, genera, and species. The class Mammalia, for example, is one of nine classes in the kingdom Animalia, phylum Chordata, subphylum Vertebrata.

From the start, Linnaeus employed Latin for his binomial nomenclature, both because Latin was commonly used by scientists at the time and because it would avoid the confusion different languages would bring. Each species is identified by a genus name and a specific epithet. For example, the domestic cat is called *Felis domesticus.*

Taxonomists—today more commonly referred to as systematists—are attempting more and more to classify mammals in a way that reflects their evolutionary history. And as information is acquired from newly discovered fossils or molecular genetics, they rearrange the current classification scheme, adding new species and moving species from one genus to another.

More than five hundred new species of mammals have been identified in the last twenty years; ten to twelve are named each year. By the classification system used in this book *(page 180)*, there are currently 4,629 known species grouped in 1,135 genera, in turn grouped in 136 families in 26 orders. These orders are then organized according to whether they belong to subclass Prototheria, which includes all monotremes *(page opposite)*, or subclass Theria. Theria includes two subgroups, known as infraclasses: Metatheria for marsupials *(page 16)* and Eutheria for placental mammals *(pages 17 to 29)*. On the following pages, all current extant families are listed according to their order; a complete list of subclasses, infraclasses, and orders is on page 180.

Monotremes

DUCK-BILLED PLATYPUS (*Ornithorhynchus anatinus*)

When the first duck-billed platypus arrived from Australia in Britain in 1798, it was assumed to be a fake, a fantastic creature with the small body of a mammal and the bill of a duck. Named *Ornithorhynchus anatinus,* the duck-billed platypus *(page 97)* has long since been classified as a monotreme, along with two species of echidnas: the Australian, or short-nosed, echidna (*Tachyglossus aculeatus*) *(page 129)* and the giant, or long-nosed, echidna of New Guinea. They are all believed to have originated in the Australian–Antarctic section of Gondwana, an ancient continental land mass that once overlay the southernmost region of the planet more than 100 million years ago *(page 36).*

Monotremes are sufficiently different in their morphology and evolution for systema-

tists to have placed them in their own subclass, called Prototheria *(page 180)*—despite controversial new DNA analysis that suggests monotremes may be more closely related to marsupials than previously thought. (This is why some classification schemes locate monotremes in subclass Theria, along with marsupials and placental mammals.)

Monotremes amble like reptiles on laterally oriented limbs. Female monotremes lay soft reptilelike eggs, incubating them much as birds do. They lack nipples, or teats, from which to suckle their newborn. Instead, milk seeps from pores in the abdomen for the young to lap up. As adults, they lack teeth— although like all other mammals, they have a single dentary bone and three middle-ear bones.

Echidnas live on land and eat termites and ants. When enemies approach, they burrow directly into the ground or roll into a spiny, protective ball. The platypus, however, is aquatic. It has a long, leathery beak covered with electroreceptors

LONG-NOSED ECHIDNA
(*Zaglossus bruijni*)

capable of detecting the electrical field of small invertebrates. All male monotremes sport spurs on their ankles, but only those of the platypus are equipped with poison glands *(page 31).*

● ● ● ● ● ● ● ● ● ● ● ● ● ● ● ● ●

ORDER: MONOTREMATA

FAMILY: TACHYGLOSSIDAE
ECHIDNAS (SPINY ANTEATERS)

ORNITHORHYNCHIDAE
DUCK-BILLED PLATYPUS

● ● ● ● ● ● ● ● ● ● ● ● ● ● ● ● ●

Marsupials

KOALA
(*Phascolarctus cinereus*)

Marsupials have developed a unique reproductive system: They give birth to altricial, or minimally developed, young that climb from the vulva of their mother into a marsupium—an abdominal pouch or fold in their mother's skin—to nurse as they continue to grow. This and other differences have persuaded systematists to place marsupials in their own separate subgroup, infraclass Metatheria *(page 180)*, and to organize them into seven orders, as shown at left below.

Since Australia drifted apart from Antarctica *(page 36)*, Australian marsupials have evolved in isolation, developing into many forms—today there are more than two hundred species that fall in four groups: the carnivorous marsupials, such as the Tasmanian devil; the bandicoot group; the marsupial mole; and the diprodonts, which include kangaroos and koalas. Many of them have assumed lifestyles similar to those lived by placentals elsewhere. For example, kangaroos—not gazelles or antelopes—graze on Australian grasslands; koalas—not monkeys—live in the trees; and there are marsupial squirrels, anteaters, moles, and cats.

In the Americas, where competition with placentals has been stiff, all but one of the seventy surviving marsupials are opossums. Nocturnal and omnivorous, they are either arboreal or terrestrial creatures, all except for the yapok (*Chironectes minimus*), which lives in the water. The Virginia opossum is the only marsupial that lives north of Mexico.

AMERICAN MARSUPIALS	
ORDER: DIDELPHIMORPHIA	
FAMILY: DIDELPHIDAE	OPOSSUMS
ORDER: PAUCITUBERCULATA	
FAMILY: CAENOLESTIDAE	RAT OPOSSUMS
ORDER: MICROBIOTHERIA	
FAMILY: MICROBIOTHERIIDAE	LLACA
AUSTRALIAN MARSUPIALS	
ORDER: DASYUROMORPHIA	
FAMILY: THYLACINIDAE	THYLACINE (EXTINCT)
MYRMECOBIIDAE	NUMBAT
DASYURIDAE	DASYURES, QUOLLS, ANTECHINUSES, TASMANIAN DEVIL
ORDER: PERAMELEMORPHIA	
FAMILY: PERAMELIDAE	BANDICOOTS
PERORYCTIDAE	BANDICOOTS
ORDER: NOTORYCTEMORPHIA	
FAMILY: NOTORYCTIDAE	MARSUPIAL "MOLE"
ORDER: DIPROTODONTIA	
FAMILY: PHASCOLARCTIDAE	KOALA
VOMBATIDAE	WOMBATS
PHALANGERIDAE	CUSCUSES, PHALANGERS
POTOROIDAE	RAT KANGAROOS, BETTONGS
MACROPODIDAE	KANGAROOS, WALLABIES
BURRAMYIDAE	PIGMY POSSUMS
PSEUDOCHEIRIDAE	RING-TAILED POSSUMS
PETAURIDAE	GLIDERS, STRIPED POSSUMS
TARSIPEDIDAE	HONEY POSSUM NOOLBENGER
ACROBATIDAE	FEATHERTAIL POSSUM, FEATHERTAIL GLIDER

VIRGINIA OPOSSUM
(*Didelphis virginiana*)

Anteaters, Sloths, & Armadillos

The twenty-nine species in the order Xenarthra are linked by their South American origins and a shared anatomical feature: uncommonly strong backbones. The xenarthrans get their name from an extra articulation, called a xenarthrous process, in their lumbar vertebrae. Apart from this skeletal characteristic, the families in this order display more differences than similarities.

Anteaters live mainly in warm and moist tropical habitats. They use their long, sharp claws to tear up hard-packed nests of ants and termites, catching the insects with their long tongue, made sticky by secretions from specialized salivary glands. Although the other three species in its family are largely arboreal, the giant anteater lives a terrestrial life. Up to about four feet (1 m) in length and weighing as much as ninety pounds (40 kg), it has an awkward gait due to its large, inwardly turned, non-retractable claws. It can, however, run surprising fast when necessary.

PALE-THROATED THREE-TOED SLOTH
(*Bradypus tridactylus*)

Sloths don't do anything fast. Notorious for their low activity level, they spend most of their time hanging upside down in trees and eating leaves in their rain-forest habitat. They are so specialized for arboreal life—possessing long fore limbs, muscles evolved for hanging, and long, curved claws—that they have difficulty moving on the ground. Armadillos have no such problem. Their powerful limbs make them fast runners. They get their name from the bony plates of jointed armor that cover their body, neck, and head. Most of the twenty armadillo species feed primarily on insects, but will also eat small vertebrates and some vegetable matter. They can be found all over South America, and extend into North America as far as Nebraska. Prolonged cold spells have been known to wipe out about two-thirds of populations living in the more northerly habitats.

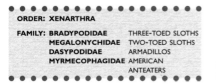

GIANT ANTEATER (*Myrmecophaga tridactyla*)

ORDER: XENARTHRA	
FAMILY: BRADYPODIDAE	THREE-TOED SLOTHS
MEGALONYCHIDAE	TWO-TOED SLOTHS
DASYPODIDAE	ARMADILLOS
MYRMECOPHAGIDAE	AMERICAN ANTEATERS

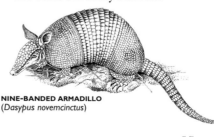

NINE-BANDED ARMADILLO
(*Dasypus novemcinctus*)

Insectivores

More than four hundred species in sixty-five genera are collected into the seven families of the order Insectivora.

EUROPEAN MOLE
(Talpa europea)

Mostly small and mobile, the members of this order represent a diverse collection of shrews, moles, hedgehogs, moonrats, tenrecs, and solenodons. All have long, narrow snouts and a refined sense of smell to help them find and root out insects. Some also eat small animals such as worms, crabs, frogs, and even fish.

For the most part, insectivores have small brains, little eyes with limited vision, and short limbs that prohibit leaping or jumping. They range in size from the pygmy shrew (*Suncus etruscus*), which measures barely two inches (5 cm) long from the top of its head to the tip of its tail and weighs about 0.7 ounce (2 g), to the moonrat *(page 101)*, which grows up to eighteen inches (45 cm) long and weighs more than two pounds (1 kg).

Found everywhere but the polar regions and Australasia, insectivores display numerous specializations.

EUROPEAN HEDGEHOG (*Erinaceus europaeus*)

ORDER: INSECTIVORA	
FAMILY: SOLENODONTIDAE	SOLENODONS
NESOPHONTIDAE	WEST INDIAN SHREWS (EXTINCT)
TENRECIDAE	TENRECS
CHRYSOCHLORIDAE	GOLDEN MOLES
ERINACEIDAE	HEDGEHOGS
SORICIDAE	SHREWS
TALPIDAE	MOLES

OLD WORLD WATER SHREW
(*Neomys fodiens*)

A number of species, including the aquatic tenrec (*Limnogale mergulus*) and the Pyrenean desman *(page 88)*, have evolved to exploit aquatic habitats. Their long tail, streamlined body, shorter limbs, and partially or fully webbed feet help them catch a variety of underwater prey. Hedgehogs and some tenrecs sport spiny coats that they can deploy to defend themselves. Moles, such as the European mole, have modified pectoral girdles and front limbs, as well as spadelike feet and heavy claws for burrowing underground. The rare and endangered solenodons of Hispaniola and Cuba *(page 102)*, together with Old World water shrews and North American short-tailed shrews (*Blarina brevicauda*), are the only mammals that produce venom in their saliva and chew it into their wounded prey.

Tree Shrews

Once grouped with the insectivores, the nineteen species of tree shrews now occupy an order of their own: Scandentia. Separated into five genera, these energetic, diurnal, and largely arboreal mammals may be a link between insectivores and primates. Small, with reddish brown coats, all tree shrews have thirty-eight sharp teeth and long, pointed muzzles. The feather-tailed species (*Ptilocercus lowii*) uses its long, scale-covered tail as an organ for support and touch, enabling it to

COMMON TREE SHREW
(*Tupaia glis*)

grab insects with a single hand. The female common tree shrew of Southeast Asia keeps her young in a separate nest and suckles them every second day.

ORDER: SCANDENTIA

FAMILY: TUPAIIDAE TREE SHREWS

Colugos

Sometimes called flying lemurs, colugos are neither lemurs nor true flyers. They are small creatures about the size of a domestic cat, with large eyes, a pointed face, and long, sharp claws. There are two kinds: a Philippine species, *Cynocephalus volans,* and the somewhat larger, paler Malaysian species, *C. variegatus.* Although they were once classified in either Insectivora or Chiroptera, they are today firmly ensconced in a separate order called Dermoptera (meaning "skin-winged"). These creatures can glide more than 320 feet (100 m) through the air, thanks

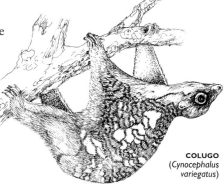

COLUGO
(*Cynocephalus variegatus*)

to a thin, fur-covered membrane that extends from behind the ears down along the sides of the body to join the legs and tail. They keep out of sight during the day and emerge to travel upside down along tree branches at night. Colugos are equipped with comblike incisors, which they use to chew on vegetation and to groom themselves.

ORDER: DERMOPTERA

FAMILY: CYNOCEPHALIDAE COLUGOS

Bats

The order Chiroptera (meaning "hand wing") contains the only true flying mammals: bats. The entire bat skeleton, especially the limbs, is modified for flight. The wings are formed from elongated finger bones (except for the thumb, which has a claw) and they are covered by flight membranes, extensions of the body's skin, which often extend between leg and tail.

Almost all bats are nocturnal, with some species flying up to fifty-six miles (90 km) each night between their feeding grounds and the caves or roosts where they sleep by day. They have good vision, but most make their way through the dark night sky with the aid of sonar or echolocation *(page 45)*.

There are more than 925 known species of bats, making this the second-largest mammalian order. It is divided into two suborders:

LESSER HORSESHOE BAT
(*Rhinolophus hipposideros*)

LITTLE BROWN BAT
(*Myotis lucifugus*)

WRINKLE-FACED BAT
(*Centurio senex*)

WAHLBERG'S EPAULETTED FRUIT BAT
(*Epomophorus wahlbergi*)

ORDER: CHIROPTERA	
FAMILY: PTEROPODIDAE	OLD WORLD FRUIT BATS, FLYING FOXES
EMBALLONURIDAE	SAC-WINGED BATS
RHINOPOMATIDAE	MOUSE-TAILED BATS
CRASEONYCTERIDAE	KITTI'S HOG-NOSED BAT
NYCTERIDAE	HOLLOW-FACED BATS, SLIT-FACED BATS
MEGADERMATIDAE	FALSE VAMPIRE BATS
RHINOLOPHIDAE	HORSESHOE BATS, OLD WORLD LEAF-NOSED BATS
PHYLLOSTOMIDAE	LEAF-NOSED BATS
MORMOOPIDAE	MUSTACHED BATS
NOCTILIONIDAE	BULLDOG BATS
MYSTACINIDAE	SHORT-TAILED BATS
MOLOSSIDAE	FREE-TAILED BATS
MYZOPODIDAE	SUCKER-FOOTED BAT
THYROPTERIDAE	DISK-WINGED BATS
FURIPTERIDAE	SMOKY BATS
NATALIDAE	FUNNEL-EARED BATS
VESPERTILIONIDAE	EVENING BATS, VESPER BATS

Megachiroptera (large bats), which has only one family, Pteropodidae; and Microchiroptera (small bats), which contains the remaining sixteen families.

Most of the 166 species of pteropids are fruit-eaters; the rest feed on nectar and pollen. They can often be recognized by their large eyes and pointed face, which have earned some of them the name "flying foxes."

Mostly small with tiny eyes—as their name suggests—the microchiropterans are mainly insectivores, although there are several notable exceptions. For example, the very large family of leaf-nosed bats, Phyllostomidae, includes many fruit-eating species as well as three species of vampire bats, which feed exclusively on the blood of birds and large mammals; and the fishing bat (*Myotis vivesi*), true to its name, eats fish.

Primates

Primates are a diverse group linked by a number of important characteristics. They have well-developed brains protected by rounded brain cases, and large, forward-facing eyes that provide them with excellent visual abilities, particularly depth perception. Largely herbivorous, many primates are omnivorous when an opportunity arises. Most have powerful hind limbs and strong, gripping hands and feet (with flat nails instead of claws), suitable for their primarily arboreal lifestyle. Although some of our closer primate relatives, such as the chimpanzee, share at least partially our terrestrial lifestyle, only *Homo sapiens* is truly bipedal.

Primates are divided into two suborders: the Strepsirhini, which includes the five lemur families (including the aye-aye) endemic to Madagascar and lorises; and the Haplorhini, which is composed of tarsiers, tamarins, New and Old World monkeys, gibbons, and great

CHIMPANZEE
(*Pan troglodytes*)

apes (such as chimpanzees, gorillas, and humans).

Lemurs and their close kin have elongated snouts that produce a foxlike face. However, it is the presence of a "tooth comb" of lower incisors and canine teeth and a "toilet claw" for grooming on the second digit of the foot that unites them. The smallest of all primates are strepsirhine: The smallest dwarf lemur rarely weighs more than 1.5 ounces (40 g).

Haplorhine primates possess sparsely haired noses and share reproductive patterns. In contrast to the general mammalian pattern of seasonal breeding, most haplorhine females have year-round sexual cycles. To prepare for fertilization, their uterus wall develops a tissue, called endometrium, that is shed every month if no fertilization occurs. Only elephant-shrews *(page 29)* also experience the copious blood loss (menstruation) that accompanies this shedding.

PROBOSCIS MONKEY
(*Nasalis larvatus*)

ORDER: PRIMATES

FAMILY:	
DAUBENTONIIDAE	AYE-AYE
LEMURIDAE	LEMURS
MEGALADAPIDAE	GIANT LEMURS
LORISIDAE	LORISES
CHEIROGALEIDAE	DWARF LEMURS
INDRIDAE	INDRI, SIFAKAS, AVAHI
TARSIIDAE	TARSIERS
CERCOPITHECIDAE	OLD WORLD MONKEYS
HOMINIDAE	APES, HUMAN
HYLOBATIDAE	GIBBONS
CALLITRICHIDAE	MARMOSETS
CEBIDAE	NEW WORLD MONKEYS

Carnivores

**ASIATIC
BLACK BEAR**
(*Ursus thibetanus*)

ORDER: CARNIVORA		
FAMILY:	FELIDAE	CATS
	VIVERRIDAE	CIVETS
	HERPESTIDAE	MONGOOSES
	HYAENIDAE	HYENAS, AARDWOLF
	CANIDAE	WOLVES, FOXES, JACKALS
	URSIDAE	BEARS, GIANT PANDA
	OTARIIDAE	EARED SEALS, FUR SEALS, SEA LIONS
	PHOCIDAE	EARLESS SEALS
	ODOBENIDAE	WALRUS
	MUSTELIDAE	WEASELS, SKUNKS, BADGERS, OTTERS
	PROCYONIDAE	RACCOONS, RINGTAIL CATS, COATIS

While most species classified under the order Carnivora are meat-eaters, this trait is not exclusive to the order. Some bats, primates, and cetaceans also eat meat. Conversely, many carnivorans are omnivorous and some, such as the herbivorous giant panda *(page 153)* and the insectivorous aardwolf (*Proteles cristatus*), no longer eat meat at all.

What makes a mammal a Carnivora is that it shares a common ancestor with other members of the order. Most of them also share certain features, including long, pointed canine teeth and special molars, or carnassials, which in most are knife-like for cutting meat guillotine-style. Among the omnivorous ursids and among

some procyonids, however, the carnassials are not nearly as sharp, better suited for crushing and pulverizing a wider choice of food.

Foot anatomy also varies between the carnivorous and the omnivorous members of this order. Although many of the predatorial felids and canids possess a five-toe formation, they have a digiti-

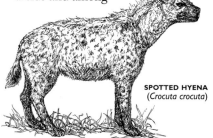

STELLER SEA LION
(*Eumetopias jubatus*)

grade stance, which keeps them on the "balls" of their feet, helping them to leap and pounce. The omnivores, such as the bears, however, tend to walk with the entire length of their feet on the ground, a plantigrade stance that provides greater stability. Carnivora's aquatic members, including the sea lion, the seal, and the walrus, naturally, have feet adapted for swimming—one of many notable morphological differences separating them from other carnivorans.

SPOTTED HYENA
(*Crocuta crocuta*)

Cetaceans

Recent molecular and paleontological studies suggest that whales, porpoises, and dolphins share a common ancestor with hippopotamuses, giraffes, and other artiodactyls. The most likely ancestral group is the Mesonychidae, which included a wolflike animal, *Mesonyx,* that ran on feet equipped with five small hoofs rather than claws. Subsequent cetacean ancestors took to the water, possibly around the time when India was still separate from Asia *(page 37).*

All cetaceans are streamlined in shape, insulated with blubber rather than hair, and equipped with a circulatory system highly adaptive to the temperature changes of the ocean. A combination of foreshortened fore limbs and unusually long digits creates rigid paddles for steering. In addition, the problem of water pressure—a formidable obstacle to deep-sea diving—has been solved by several adaptations, including

BOTTLENOSE DOLPHIN
(Tursiops truncatus)

the ability to make use of oxygen stored in the muscles and the ability to collapse the lungs rapidly.

Cetaceans either possess baleen plates or they have teeth. Baleen whales use their plates of keratin to filter small invertebrates from seawater. The 120-ton blue whale *(page 174)* has more than three hundred baleen plates in each side of its upper jaw—surprisingly, about the same number as its much smaller relative, the minke whale.

Toothed cetaceans pursue fish and other marine animals for food, rather than swimming through concentrations of plankton as do baleen whales. Having to hunt for food has caused them to develop superior swimming techniques. Porpoises can swim up

ORDER: CETACEA

TOOTHED WHALES (ODONTOCETI)	
FAMILY: PHYSETERIDAE	SPERM WHALES
ZIPHIIDAE	BEAKED WHALES
PLATANISTIDAE	RIVER DOLPHINS
DELPHINIDAE	OCEAN DOLPHINS
MONODONTIDAE	NARWHAL, BELUGA
PHOCOENIDAE	PORPOISES
BALEEN WHALES (MYSTICETI)	
FAMILY: BALAENOPTERIDAE	RORQUALS
ESCHRICHTIIDAE	GRAY WHALE
BALAENIDAE	RIGHT WHALES
NEOBALAENIDAE	PYGMY RIGHT WHALES

MINKE WHALE
(Balaenoptera acutorostrata)

to twenty-eight miles (45 km) per hour. Similar speeds have been observed in bottlenose dolphins, which pursue fish onto mudflats, sliding right out of the water to seize their prey.

Sirenians

Once an order with five species, Sirenia now has four: three species of manatee (genus *Trichechus*) and one of dugong (genus *Dugong*). The fifth species, the Steller's sea cow, was hunted to extinction in the early eighteenth century.

DUGONG (*Dugong dugon*)

Sirenians swim in the coastal waters of Central and South America, Asia, India, and Africa. The dugong inhabits marine waters, while the manatee *(page 174)* prefers freshwater coastal rivers and estuaries. Size is the only defense of sirenians: Adults range from five hundred to thirty-five hundred pounds (230 to 1,600 kg). The fore-runners of sirenians are believed to have descended from an ancestor shared with elephants. Resembling a cross between a seal and a hippopotamus, the sirenian has a streamlined body with no external ears, or pinnae. Its nostrils are located on top of the head. Sensory bristles on its large upper snout are similar to those of a pig or a cow.

ORDER: SIRENIA

FAMILY: DUGONGIDAE   DUGONGS, SEA COWS
TRICHECHIDAE   MANATEES

Elephants

The family Elephantidae consists of only two species, but the fossil record shows that it may have once included as many as 350. The most evident difference between the two surviving species is size. The larger African elephant has much bigger ears, or pinnae, which help to cool it down and to trap sounds over long distances. The most prominent feature of both elephants, however, is the trunk, or proboscis—hence their order's

AFRICAN ELEPHANT
(*Loxodonta africana*)

ASIAN ELEPHANT
(*Elephas maximus*)

name. An estimated forty thousand muscles make the trunk the most versatile of appendages—strong enough to lift heavy objects, yet deft enough to pick up a coin. Indispensable in the elephant's daily life, it is used for defense, smelling, drinking, feeding, and sound production.

ORDER: PROBOSCIDEA

FAMILY: ELEPHANTIDAE   ELEPHANTS

Ungulates

Hooves are modified toenails, and the mammals that walk on them are called ungulates. Ungulates are typically herbivorous and are adapted for running. They are classified into two orders: Perissodactyla and Artiodactyla. Although the perissodactyls were originally—during the early Tertiary period—the more abundant of the two orders, they later declined for unknown reasons, while the artiodactyls flourished and diversified. Today there are 17 perissodactyl species and more than 220 species of artiodactyls.

Perissodactyls have either one weight-bearing toe, such as the horse, or three weight-bearing toes, such as the rhinoceros and the tapir, which also has a fourth toe and vestiges of a fifth toe on the front foot.

The tapir's largest relative is the 2.3-ton white rhinoceros (*Ceratotherium simum*), which, unlike the aggressive black rhinoceros, is mild and inoffensive. It has even bigger ancestors, including the largest known land mammal, *Indricotherium*, a brute of a herbivore that may have weighed twenty tons. Although this ancient giant lacked horns, today's rhinos have either single or double horns, both of which lack a bony core and are made up of countless hollow filaments extending from the skin.

Horns and antlers are perhaps the most visually outstanding feature of many artiodactyls. Giraffes, pronghorns, and all wild bovids are among those that have bony horns sheathed in keratin or covered in furred skin. The horns themselves are never shed, although pronghorns shed their sheaths annually.

Antlers, however, are shed annually in the winter. Mostly males grow antlers and their presence is found in all but two species in the family Cervidae, a group that includes deer, wapiti, and caribou. Secretions from the pituitary gland initiate the growth of the antlers in the spring and they continue to grow until the rut in the fall, when the males use them in clashes with each other during competition for females.

Artiodactyls are defined by the structure of

BLACK RHINOCEROS
(*Diceros bicornis*)

ORDER: PERISSODACTYLA (ODD-TOED UNGULATES)	
FAMILY: EQUIDAE	HORSES, ASSES, ZEBRAS
TAPIRIDAE	TAPIR
RHINOCEROTIDAE	RHINOCEROSES
ORDER: ARTIODACTYLA	(EVEN-TOED UNGULATES)
FAMILY: SUIDAE	SWINE
TAYASSUIDAE	PECCARIES, JAVELINAS
HIPPOPOTAMIDAE	HIPPOPOTAMUSES
CAMELIDAE	CAMELS, LLAMAS
TRAGULIDAE	CHEVROTAINS
GIRAFFIDAE	GIRAFFE, OKAPI
MOSCHIDAE	MUSK DEER
CERVIDAE	DEER
ANTILOCAPRIDAE	PRONGHORNS
BOVIDAE	ANTELOPE, BISON, CATTLE, GOATS, SHEEP

their feet. Unlike perissodactyls, they bear their weight primarily on toes three and four; the big toe is always missing. Some species, including pigs, peccaries, and hippopotamuses, possess two additional complete digits on each foot. On others, namely bovids, deer, giraffes, and camels, these lateral toes are either absent or incomplete. The artiodactyls' articulation of bones and ligaments allows them to flex and extend the foot and digits—perfect for springing away from predators. However, not all artiodactyls get around in the same way: Possibly as an adaptation for locomotion on shifting sands, the camel has developed a digitigrade posture, meaning it moves on the "balls" of its feet like cats and dogs.

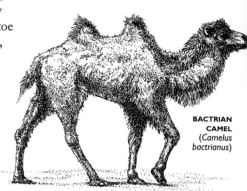

BACTRIAN CAMEL
(*Camelus bactrianus*)

Many artiodactyls belong to the suborder Ruminantia and they have a complex digestive system, characterized by the regurgitation and rechewing of food in a three- or four-chambered stomach, which harbors microorganisms for breaking down cellulose *(page 33)*.

Hyraxes

TREE HYRAX
(*Dendrohyrax dorsalis*)

ORDER: **HYRACOIDEA**

FAMILY: **PROCAVIIDAE** HYRAXES

These herbivores are believed to share common ancestry with ungulates or possibly elephants and manatees. Six species of hyrax inhabit parts of Africa and the Middle East. Stocky and muscular with a thick neck, they have short tails and flat, almost hooflike nails on most of their digits, except for those on their inner hind toes, which are long and clawlike and used for grooming. Both the tree hyrax and the rock hyrax *(page 123)* have poor thermoregulatory abilities; in inclement weather, they remain underground in their burrows, huddling together for warmth. When the hyrax engages in aggressive displays, a dark patch of hair on its back stands erect, exposing a gland—the function of which is unknown, but may be related to some recognition ritual.

Aardvarks

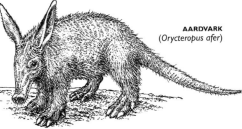

AARDVARK
(*Orycteropus afer*)

The aardvark truly stands alone: one species and one family in an order all its own. It lives in those parts of Africa richly supplied with its chief food: ants and termites. Once classified with anteaters *(page 17)* and pangolins *(below)*, with which it shares many physical and behavioral characteristics, the aardvark was eventually assigned to its own order when those similarities were found to be the result of convergent evolution *(page 37)* rather than common origin. Possessed of a medium-sized stocky build, the aardvark (an Afrikaner word meaning "earth pig") has a long, muscular tail, donkeylike ears, a narrow snout, and a long, sticky tongue specialized for catching insects underground. Its teeth, from which the order's name is derived, are tubelike molars, adapted for crushing hard-backed insects.

ORDER: TUBULIDENTATA

FAMILY: ORYCTEROPODIDAE AARDVARK

Pangolins

The seven species of pangolins, also known as scaly anteaters, are specialized for ant and termite eating. Manidae, the only family in the order, has one genus, *Manis*, which includes those living in Southeast Asia, and an African species that inhabits that continent's tropical and subtropical regions.

The body of a pangolin is covered in sharp, horny scales, giving it a distinctly reptilian appearance. Its conical skull and long tongue and tail only reinforce that false impression. Like the aardvark *(above)* and the ant- and termite-eating xenarthrans *(page 17)*, pangolins tear open termite mounds and ant hills with powerful limbs and long, sharp claws. They capture their prey with the aid of their elongated snout and their long and sticky tongue, which is anchored to their pelvis. To make up for their lack of teeth, pangolins ingest small pebbles, which help break down the hard insects in the lower parts of their stomach.

CAPE PANGOLIN
(*Manis temminckii*)

ORDER: PHOLIDOTA

FAMILY: MANIDAE PANGOLINS

Rodents

EUROPEAN HARVEST MOUSE
(*Micromys minutus*)

About 40 percent of all mammals are rodents, making Rodentia, with 2,024 species, the largest order of mammals. In adapting to so many different environments, rodents have evolved characteristics similar to those of mammals from other orders that fill similar types of habitats. One example of convergent development involves the semi-aquatic capybara, which is a forager of succulents in marshes and river beds, thus filling a similar ecological niche in South America as the hippopotamus does in Africa. Although the capybara, at about 145 pounds (66 kg), is the largest rodent, most members of the order, such as the European harvest mouse, weigh less than five ounces (150 g). This generally small size has helped rodent families radiate into a wide range of habitats and microhabitats.

All rodents lack canines; instead they have a pair of sharp incisors, which are constantly growing to compensate for being continually worn down by digging and by gnawing on coarse vegetation. Taxonomists divide Rodentia into two suborders based on the different ways the lateral and deep masseters, or jaw muscles, move and close the jaws: Sciurognathi, which includes squirrels, beavers, and the mouselike murids that make up 66 percent of the entire order; and Hystricognathi, which includes porcupines, a group of highly specialized African mole-rats, and fourteen widely radiated South American rodent families.

ORDER: RODENTIA	
FAMILY: APLODONTIDAE	MOUNTAIN BEAVER
SCIURIDAE	SQUIRRELS
CASTORIDAE	BEAVERS
GEOMYIDAE	POCKET GOPHERS
HETEROMYIDAE	KANGAROO RATS, POCKET MICE
DIPODIDAE	JUMPING MICE, JERBOAS
MURIDAE	RATS, MICE
ANOMALURIDAE	SCALY-TAILED FLYING SQUIRRELS
PEDETIDAE	SPRINGHAAS, SPRINGHARE
CTENODACTYLIDAE	GUNDIS
MYOXIDAE	DORMICE
BATHYERGIDAE	MOLE-RATS, SAND RATS
HYSTRICIDAE	OLD WORLD PORCUPINES
PETROMURIDAE	ROCK RAT
THRYONOMYIDAE	CANE RATS
ERETHIZONTIDAE	NEW WORLD PORCUPINES
CHINCHILLIDAE	CHINCHILLAS, VISCACHAS
DINOMYIDAE	PACARANA
CAVIIDAE	CUIS, CAVIES, GUINEA PIGS
HYDROCHAERIDAE	CAPYBARA
DASYPROCTIDAE	PACAS
AGOUTIDAE	AGOUTIS
CTENOMYIDAE	TUCO-TUCOS
OCTODONTIDAE	DEGUS
ABROCOMIDAE	CHINCHILLA RATS
ECHIMYIDAE	SPINY RATS
CAPROMYIDAE	HUTIAS
HEPTAXODONTIDAE	HUTIAS (EXTINCT)
MYOCASTORIDAE	NUTRIA, COYPU

CAPYBARA
(*Hydrochaeris hydrochaeris*)

Lagomorphs

SNOWSHOE HARE
(Lepus americanus)

In terms of
numbers, rabbits
and hares—
the most
well-known members of order
Lagomorpha—have proved very
successful in a variety of habitats,
particularly the limited one of the
grassland herbivore, a niche also
filled by ungulates. Still, the order
has only two families: Leporidae
and Ochotonidae. The physical
features of leporids include the
familiar oversized ears, large
incisors, and elongated hind limbs
that give it its characteristic bounding gait. Less obvious is the second
pair of incisors behind the first and

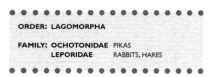

ORDER: **LAGOMORPHA**

FAMILY: **OCHOTONIDAE** PIKAS
LEPORIDAE RABBITS, HARES

the leporid skull, which is jointed,
allowing for a slight movement of
the upper and lower jaws.

The twenty-six species of picas
in Ochotonidae look more like
small, tail-less rodents than their
rabbit cousins. North American
picas inhabit boreal or alpine
biomes; Eurasian species occupy
more varied habitats,
including forests,
plains, and
desert steppes.

**BLACK-TAILED
JACKRABBIT**
(Lepus californicus)

Elephant-Shrews

The fifteen living species of
elephant-shrews were once classified with other insectivores, but
recent molecular and morphological studies have shown that these
African mammals have no close
relatives and merit their own order.

Size varies considerably among
elephant-shrews, ranging from the
1.5-ounce (45-g) *Elephantulus rozeti*
to the one-pound (0.5-kg) golden-
rumped elephant-shrew *Rhynchocyon
chrysopygus (page 117)*. Recognized by
their long snout and large
eyes, elephant-shrews are
prodigious hunters of
small invertebrates,
using their long fore-

ORDER: **MACROSCELIDEA**

FAMILY: **MACROSCELIDIDAE** ELEPHANT-SHREWS

foot claws to forage in leaf litter or
soil. Their long limbs enable them
to bound from predators at surprising speed. They occupy many different habitats, including open plains,
savannas, deserts, thornbush, and
tropical forests, where they create
and scrupulously maintain a network of trails along the ground
within their home territory. Both
sexes are believed to mark
their territory with scent
and sometimes feces.

RUFOUS ELEPHANT-SHREW
(Elephantulus rufescens)

Inconspicuous Beginnings

As early as 300 million years ago, the pelycosaur *Dimetrodon* showed some mammalian tendencies. This one-quarter-ton scaly beast carried a ribbed sail on its back that probably absorbed solar energy, enabling it to heat up more quickly than its competitors. With rudimentary circulatory control to delay heat loss, the ten-foot (3-m) -long animal that lived over much of the land that is now North America is believed by some scientists to be a precursor of warm-blooded mammals. Fossil records from about a million years later suggest that relatives of the pelycosaurs, the therapsids—animals from a different order, but within the same subclass, Synapsida—had evolved mammalian-like teeth and a lower jaw bone that foreshadowed the dentary bone that characterizes mammals *(page 9)*. These precursors are called cynodonts, and from their stock evolved the first true mammals.

Although neither hair nor mammary glands are preserved in the fossil record, the fossilized bones of the early Jurassic Morganucodon *suggest that this creature possessed both—and so is one of the earliest true mammals.*

MINIATURE SURVIVORS

Dinosaurs flourished during the Jurassic period (180 to 135 million years ago), ruling the world from the top (and bottom) of the food chain. Our ancestors may have survived this reign of terror by becoming small enough to escape notice. One therapsid in the lineage—a cynodont called *Cynognathus*—may have had hair to insulate its small, possibly warm-blooded body. This warmth could have enabled *Cynognathus* to prowl more successfully during colder but safer nights. Its descendants include *Morganucodon*, which lived about 195 million years ago. This shrewlike creature measured about 5.5 inches (14 cm) long and hunted insects and perhaps baby reptiles.

Mammals evolved an ability to chew food thoroughly. Over time, openings in the skull for nasal passages shifted to permit breathing and chewing at the same time. *Morganucodon* already had a variety of teeth—from canines to incisors to molars—as well as jawbone attachments suitable for difficult chewing. These early mammals even exhibited the juvenile milk teeth suitable only for a nursing period. In fact, evidence of the ability to lactate has been uncovered among mammals' ancestors well before 180 million years ago.

Morganucodon skeletons also show mammals' early penchant for speed and agility: Legs began to swing back and forth rather than outward, thus eliminating the ancestral side-to-side amble. This required adjustments in hip and pelvic structure. Along the way, mammals also developed differentiated vertebrae, enhancing motor control. And these early mammals had a distinctive lower jaw that terminated in three tiny bones—the malleus, the incus, and the stapes—suited for amplifying sounds in the ear.

Mammals were thus poised to take over following the sudden demise of the dinosaurs around sixty-five million years ago, and they multiplied and diversified. Within three million years some mammals were as big as wolves. Some learned to fly and others turned to the ocean. One swimming ancestor of the whale is *Basilosaurus* of the Eocene epoch, which began about fifty-eight million years ago. Its fifty-five-foot (17-m) -long skeleton included hindlegs as well as front legs with digits.

Teeth continued to mark the evolution of mammals. For example, four unrelated early mammals developed long tearing teeth—saber teeth—in a process called convergent evolution: They lacked a common fanged ancestor, but living in similar habitats, these mammals began to look and behave similarly. All four saber-toothed mammals subsequently became extinct, possibly because of the demise of their favorite prey.

The number of mammal species has dwindled greatly since the first explosion of mammalian forms more than fifty million years ago. Today one mammal—the human—is ascendant in a world that never again will see such cousins as the giant sloth or the four-tusked elephant.

Species in Flux

In 1857 British naturalist Charles Darwin published his theory of evolution in a book called *On the Origin of the Species*. In this controversial document, he drew on observations he made during a round-the-world voyage, countless discussions with animal and plant breeders, and evidence in the fossil record to argue that individual species are not fixed, but constantly changing over time. He believed that these changes were made possible by the mechanism of natural selection, whereby individuals with traits that enhance reproduction and survival are more likely to pass on these characteristics to the next generation.

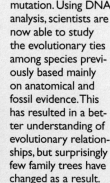

Thus, proportions of these adaptive traits—longer horns, sharper beaks—change in the population over time, and so does the species. Later biologists, through the study of genetics, have come to understand that evolution depends on the natural selection of variants of genes responsible for advantageous characteristics and that new variants are initiated by genetic mutation. Using DNA analysis, scientists are now able to study the evolutionary ties among species previously based mainly on anatomical and fossil evidence. This has resulted in a better understanding of evolutionary relationships, but surprisingly few family trees have changed as a result.

Eating

Only a few mammals don't chew their food. The mouth of baleen whales, for instance, harbors plates of tough skinlike material (baleen) with hairlike fringes to filter plankton from seawater.

Most mammals are fairly catholic in their tastes—as long as the food falls into the right food group. While carnivores such as canids prefer to eat the flesh of other mammals, they also enjoy fish and insects and will feed on the gut of their prey even when it's full of plant matter. Even the zebra-loving lion will devour a distasteful human when it is too old to catch anything else. Omnivores such as bears are opportunistic and can thrive on a variable mix of meat and plants. Herbivores, however, usually restrict their diet to plants—except those female herbivores that eat their placenta after birth. A few herbivores are so strict that they'll turn up their nose at most other food, preferring one specific kind of plant. Giant pandas primarily eat bamboo, for instance, and koalas feed only on a few species of smooth-barked eucalyptus trees.

A mammal that has evolved to eat only insects dines frequently. Anteaters can digest as much as one pound (0.5 kg) of ants at a time. After an anteater rips open a nest, it plunges in its snout and uses its long sticky tongue to garner the meal. Most herbivores keep busy foraging because plants are relatively low-energy food compared to protein-rich flesh. The African elephant must snack nearly incessantly to get about 330 pounds (150 kg) of grass and shrubs a day, while the lion makes one big meal of zebra or other meat and then spends days lolling about without hunting.

A catnap is time well spent, however, for catching meat requires effort

Adaptations for Eating

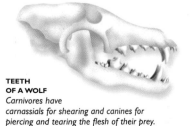

**TEETH
OF A WOLF**
Carnivores have carnassials for shearing and canines for piercing and tearing the flesh of their prey.

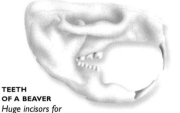

**TEETH
OF A BEAVER**
Huge incisors for gnawing wood dominate the muzzle of the canineless beaver. It keeps debris out of its throat by drawing its lips into the space left by the absent canines.

and skill. Because lions often run several miles an hour slower than their prey, they resort to surprise, showing great patience as they creep slowly up on a herd.

Mammals need much of their dinner as fuel to maintain body temperature; they cannot afford to waste energy on digestion. Many herbivores let chewing take care of the problem, easing the burden on stomach and intestines. In fact, all mammals grow at least two sets of teeth over a lifetime. In front are the incisors. Among some mammals, especially rodents, these sharp teeth are ever-growing. Beside and behind the incisors are canines, teeth well suited for stabbing meat. Behind them are the cheek teeth: premolars, which tear, and molars, which grind. Herbivores such as horses often have so-called lophodont molars—molars with grinding cusps—to help break down the silica crystals in plants, while carnivores have specialized teeth called carnassials—consisting of an upper premolar and a lower molar—that enable them to slice meat efficiently.

Mammals also have an impressive variety of inner digestive systems.

Herbivores do the hardest work—masticating raw plant fiber so their digestive system can extract nutrients. Lacking enzymes, they enlist the help of bacteria to break down the cellulose. In horses, this fermentation occurs in the large intestine, after the food has been chewed and passed through gastric juices in the stomach. The nutrients are absorbed into the bloodstream across the

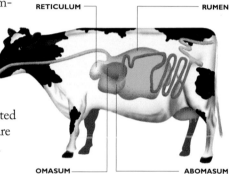

RETICULUM RUMEN

OMASUM ABOMASUM

A Four-chambered Stomach
After storing food to ferment in the reticulum and the rumen, the cow regurgitates it to chew again. Only then is the food ready to pass into the omasum and the abomasum and onto the intestines for absorption into the body.

intestinal walls. Ruminants such as cows and giraffes chew only lightly before food goes to the stomach, which is usually four-chambered. It may take them up to a hundred hours to fully digest a meal, as opposed to between thirty and forty-five hours for a horse.

TEETH OF A GIRAFFE
The herbivorous giraffe has splayed canine teeth for grabbing thorny plants and molars with rounded crowns for mastication.

TOOTHLESS ANTEATER
The anteater gathers ants with a tongue that is more than twelve inches (30 cm) longer than its twenty-inch (50 cm) snout.

From Here to There

Adult humans, alone among mammals, walk on two limbs all the time. This style of locomotion is considered a symbol of evolutionary superiority since it frees a pair of limbs for other uses. But other mammals employ a wide array of efficient methods of locomotion to perform feats well beyond the capabilities of humanity.

Most mammals are tetrapods—that is, four-footed. This makes evolutionary sense, given that the ancestors of all terrestrial vertebrates are descended from fishes, four fins of which eventually evolved into four limbs. Even cetaceans and sirenians were once terrestrial tetrapods before they took to the sea.

Being four-legged means that the most characteristic movements of mammals are walking and running. Humans—like bears, among others—plant their feet flat on the ground, a stable configuration for walking. But dogs and cats move on their toes, hocks eternally raised in a running position. Horses, deer,

and antelope walk on the toenails of one digit and so take tiptoeing to a pointed extreme. They also have limiting joints that hinge their feet, and they can't flop their wrists or ankles. Instead, their limbs are braced for the efficiency of back and forth flexing, essential for forward propulsion. Furthermore, a large portion of their leg-muscle mass is positioned relatively high on the limb, meaning that the animal swings a lighter load and thus moves fast and stops quickly.

Speedy mammals also often have long limbs hinged on a fulcrumlike joint, which yields maximum quickness when the muscles pull. Tendons store and release energy with each step, and shoulders or hips rock back and forth to extend the stride. One feature that gives horses, elephants, and other large mammals great endurance is a stiff back and relatively straight legs. This served them well when habitat changes starting millions of years ago meant they had to cover great distances in search of grass to graze on.

Adaptations for Locomotion

**BACK PAW
OF A SEA OTTER**
Only the back paws are webbed for swimming; its front paws are clawed for grasping food.

**BACK FOOT OF
A DUCK-BILLED PLATYPUS**
Front and back feet are webbed for swimming, but only the back feet of the males are also equipped with poison spurs.

**FRONT HOOF OF
AN ARABIAN CAMEL**
Unlike other ungulates, which run on their toenails, camels run on the balls of their feet.

**FRONT HOOF
OF A RHINOCEROS**
The hooves of ungulates, whether even- or odd-toed, serve them well for running on flat land.

**LENGTHENED FOREARM
HELPS SUPPORT
FLIGHT MEMBRANE**

**MODIFIED THUMB
HAS A CLAW IN
MOST BAT SPECIES**

**FLIGHT MEMBRANE
CONTAINS A HIGH CONCEN-
TRATION OF BLOOD VESSELS**

*Although there are mammals
that can glide, such as the American
flying squirrel, the Australian honey
glider, and the colugos, only the bat has
achieved true flight. Its wings are modified hands: The digits (except the thumbs) are
elongated to form struts to support the membrane, which is an extension of the bat's skin.*

The cheetah has a supple back that arches as the legs are pulled underneath, then releases and stretches as the cat lunges ahead. A champion sprinter, it is the fastest mammal—streaking along at top speeds of almost seventy miles (110 km) per hour. In fifteen-second bursts, the cheetah can catch a Thomson's gazelle, an animal that can reach fifty miles (80 km) per hour, but usually travels more slowly since it is often weighed down with semi-digested plant food.

Getting around on all fours may be the most common form of locomotion, but when up on two feet, a red kangaroo (*Macropus rufus*) can hop its way to Olympic gold at about forty miles (64 km) per hour. The kangaroo also has a vertical leap of more than ten feet (3 m)—about triple that of Michael Jordan—and at top speed, it may bound almost fifty-six feet (14 m) per hop. When a kangaroo walks, it gets down on all fives: It balances on its heavy tail and fore limbs while swinging its back feet forward to step ahead.

A variety of mammals that have abandoned ground in favor of an arboreal life use a tail as a grasping limb. Woolly monkeys are particularly adept climbers with their tail. The gibbon does well enough without, leaping more than twenty feet (6 m) between handholds in trees. Its small thumbs slip out of the way as it swings from grip to grip.

Aquatic mammals use a wide range of motions. A sea lion paddles with its fore limbs and steers with its hind limbs, while a walrus propels itself with all four flippers. A whale's hind limbs have been modified into paddlelike flukes that give enough propulsive force to move it at more than thirty miles (50 km) per hour.

**HIND FOOT OF
A CHIMPANZEE**
*Both the hands and feet of
many primates are equipped
with opposable thumbs and
toes for greater dexterity.*

**FRONT CLAW OF
A THREE-TOED SLOTH**
*Long, sturdy claws allow
the sloth to rip open
termite and ant nests.*

35

Moving with the Times

Charles Darwin began to formulate his theory of evolution by natural selection *(page 31)* while on a five-year (1831 to 1836) journey around the globe aboard the HMS *Beagle*. While on this cruise of discovery, Darwin stopped in South America and unearthed a fossil of an extinct form of horse. How could a horse have lived in the Americas long before the Spaniards introduced the animal during their sixteenth-century conquests? More than a century would pass before scientists figured out what was behind Darwin's discovery and were able to show how the horse—and other mammals—came to be distributed across the continents.

DRIFTING CONTINENTS

Since time immemorial, Earth's land masses have been on the move. Over hundreds of millions of years, they joined, split up, and reconfigured, creating first one, then another supercontinent. Early mammals were evolving when the supercontinent known as Pangaea— made up of North America, South America, Europe, and Africa—existed during the early Mesozoic (about 200 million years ago). Though relatively few in number, these Mesozoic mammals were free to spread across the continents. However, it was only after the extinction of the dinosaurs sixty-

five million years ago that the mammals began to proliferate, and by then the continents had already drifted apart.

The warm "greenhouse" climate of the Mesozoic continued well after the disappearance of the dinosaurs. Lemur-like mammals, palm trees, crocodiles, and coral reefs thrived as far north as the Arctic circle until about fifty million years ago. Then, as the continents continued to separate and drift northward, the Earth's climate cooled. Ice sheets formed on Antarctica as early as about thirty-four million years ago.

New land connections were made as the continents moved apart. Land bridges formed, disappeared, and reformed, allowing mammals to travel between Africa and Eurasia, Asia and North America, and eventually between South America and North America.

Midway through the Cretaceous (136 to 65 million years ago), ancestors of present-day marsupials emerged in North America. Eventually they migrated southward, crossing over to

Fifty million years ago, a land bridge enabled tapirs to cross from their native North America to Asia. Today there are no tapirs in North America; they exist only in Central and South America and in Southeast Asia because cooling climate forced them toward the tropics.

The red arrows indicate the major land bridges that emerged during the Paleocene and early Eocene, some ten or so million years after the extinction of the dinosaurs. The yellow arrows indicate the directions taken by the continents as they drifted apart.

(about thirty two million years ago). Fossils of extinct mammals related to present-day South American species—two marsupials and a sloth, among others—have turned up on the Antarctic Peninsula, then covered by a cool temperate rain forest.

Mammals also took advantage of land bridges connecting eastern North America and Europe via Greenland and Scandinavia and linking Alaska and Siberia. The Bering land bridge, as this latter bridge is sometimes called, was the route taken by the descendants of Darwin's fossilized horse as they left North America during the Pliocene (two to five million years ago), perhaps passing the spectacled bear, *Tremarctos*, as it arrived from Asia. The ancestors of many present-day North American mammals, including deer, bison, and voles, are known to have made this trek from Asia to North America.

Antarctica and from there to Australia before that land floated away as an island. Unique forms of marsupials evolved there in the near-absence of competition from primates, ungulates, and other mammals; some, such as the Tasmanian wolf and the carnivorous kangaroo, are now extinct. They developed a range of lifestyles, duplicating forms and modes of living that existed elsewhere: Such convergent evolution produced anteaters in five different mammalian orders in the southern hemisphere alone.

Evolving alongside Australia's marsupials were the monotremes, which are believed to have originated on that continent—although a fossilized platypus forebear has been recently discovered in Patagonia, suggesting that at least some monotremes made the journey across Antarctica from Australia.

Land bridges continued to emerge intermittently between South America and Antarctica until the middle enozoic

Perhaps the most dramatic dispersal of mammals occurred when the Isthmus of Panama became dry land almost three million years ago. Called the Great American Interchange, this massive exchange involved mammals, such as the far-traveling spectacled bear, the raccoon, and the llama, moving from North America to South America, and the opossum and the armadillo—to name just a few—making the journey north from South America.

Nature Red in Tooth & Claw

Predators must be very good at what they do in order to survive. Each species has special talents that lead it to a good meal. Many have a keen sense of smell *(page 50)* and sight *(page 47)* to help locate prey. Some bats, for instance, use their sonarlike capabilities to track insects in flight *(page 45)*. But finding prey is only a beginning; it also has to be chased down. While a female lion is slower than a zebra—one of its preferred prey—it can accelerate far more quickly. If the lion creeps close enough, it can capture by ambush, particularly if it has the cooperation of several other members of its pride. On the other hand, a pack of African wild dogs has great stamina and may run for hours to wear down prey.

Unless they hunt in packs, most mammals—with the exception of shrews and weasels—rarely attempt to kill animals larger than themselves. Yet even subduing smaller prey requires special tools. Most predators have large canines to pierce tough skin. Bears not only have long teeth, but they also possess claws good for rooting out bugs or tearing flesh. Cats often use their shorter claws to grip their victim while they deliver a killing bite to the nape. Sometimes neither teeth nor claws actually do the killing. Large felines may clamp the throat of their victim with their teeth, not to draw blood but to suffocate their prey. They do not always face a struggle: Animals will often go limp with shock when held in the jaws of a lion. A canid, too, will induce shock in its prey by a combination of nose and throat holds before it disembowels the soft exposed parts.

While teeth are primarily designed for eating, they are frequently used to intimidate. Much of the apparent violence in the mammal world can be related

The gray wolf (Canis lupus) *hunts in a pack. It uses its powerful jaws to crush both hoof and bone, maximizing the food intake of every kill.*

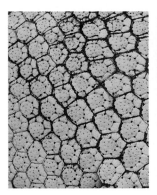

An armadillo's protective armor (far left) is made up of bony plates arranged in a variety of patterns joined together by flexible skin. By contrast, the scales of the pangolin (near left) are made up of densely massed hair. As well as shielding the body, the pangolin's scales, with their razor-sharp edges, are used as a weapon.

to neither offense nor defense, but to mammals establishing a position within the hierarchy of the group *(page 60)*. Many species, including felids, canids, and primates, bare their teeth in a show of strength, particularly within their own group. Male walruses wage battle with their tusks, which are actually modified canines. Elephants will turn their tusks—modified incisors—on lions that try to steal their calves.

A MILLION AND ONE WAYS

Hunters that rely on surprise need camouflage. When stalking a seal, the white polar bear reduces telltale shadows by lying low against the snow. And a leopard's spotted fur mixes with the dappled pattern produced by sunlight around its perch.

Camouflage is a trait that can also foil hunters. The elusive okapi uses a combination of stripes and patches of dark coloring. Near a tree in open sunlight, it melds into the shadow. An opossum calls on its theatrical ability to escape notice. It pretends it is dead and will defecate to produce an off-putting odor—a prop for an act that can last for hours.

Play acting is unnecessary for the two-ton rhinoceros, which adds a thick hide to its already intimidating appearance. The three-banded armadillo steps up the defense offered by its tough protective plates by rolling into an impenetrable ball, sometimes leaving a small trap opening in the plates that will snap shut on a probing paw or snout.

Internal armor protects the West African shrew. The six-inch (15-cm) -long creature has an interlocking backbone structure that can withstand the full weight of a human. The European hedgehog has protective hairs—hairs modified into light, stiff, sharp-tipped hollow tubes. When threatened, it curls into a ball while its muscles make these barbs stand on end—enough to dissuade the hungriest predator. The echidna also shields itself with a thick coat of barbs, but first it digs into the dirt to hide its vulnerable underside. The crested porcupine, on the other hand, won't lie still. When provoked, it rear-ends its attacker, which can receive a hide full of twenty-inch (50-cm) -long quills—a wound that can be fatal.

Reproduction & Gestation

Mammal offspring may develop in three different ways: Monotremes lay rubbery-shelled eggs that the mother incubates and hatches outside her body; in marsupials, the young develop mostly in the mother's outer pouch; and in placental mammals (including humans), the young remain inside the mother's uterus until they are more fully developed. The beginning of the story is always the same, however. First, in the process called ovulation, an egg is expelled from an ovary and travels through a fallopian tube toward the uterus, which is connected via the vagina to an opening in the pelvic area. Fertilization occurs in the fallopian tube when one of millions of sperm ejaculated from the male's penis during copulation succeeds in penetrating the egg.

EGG LIFE

The onset of regular ovulation, or sexual maturity, typically begins about fourteen years after birth for female humans. By contrast, European lemmings (*Lemmus sibiricus*), which rarely live more than a year, reach puberty less than three weeks after birth and usually have multiple litters.

Most mammal species reproduce in certain seasons. In these cases, the males do not produce sperm and the females do not ovulate the rest of the year. Humans, Old

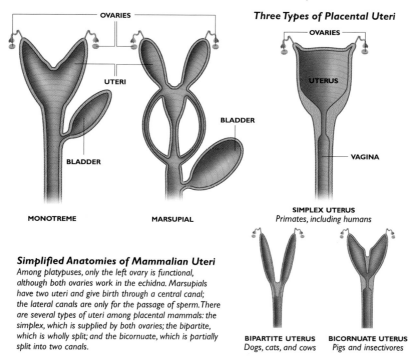

Simplified Anatomies of Mammalian Uteri
Among platypuses, only the left ovary is functional, although both ovaries work in the echidna. Marsupials have two uteri and give birth through a central canal; the lateral canals are only for the passage of sperm. There are several types of uteri among placental mammals: the simplex, which is supplied by both ovaries; the bipartite, which is wholly split; and the bicornuate, which is partially split into two canals.

MONOTREME **MARSUPIAL**

Three Types of Placental Uteri

SIMPLEX UTERUS
Primates, including humans

BIPARTITE UTERUS
Dogs, cats, and cows

BICORNUATE UTERUS
Pigs and insectivores

Risky Business

During their lengthy gestation of 110 days (two weeks more than the larger lion), spotted hyenas (page 22) are exposed to high levels of testosterone, resulting in females with fearsome dispositions and masculinized genitalia: They urinate, copulate, and give birth through a penislike clitoris. Not surprisingly, there is a high rate of mortality among females giving birth for the first time.

most lagomorphs only complete ovulation following copulation. They are nonetheless far more prolific egg-releasers than various marsupial mice, which reproduce only once in a lifetime.

When placental mammals ovulate, estrogen released from the ovary causes the walls of the uterus to thicken with a mesh of tiny blood vessels. If a sperm successfully merges with the nucleus of the egg, the resulting fertilized egg will nestle into the wall of the uterus. A thinly layered wall of tissue, called the placenta, connects embryo and mother, with nutrients and oxygen from the mother's blood passing through this tissue.

MULTIPLE METHODS

The various phases of reproduction do not always proceed steadily to birth. After copulating, many bats delay fertilization: Sperm wait in the uterus of the silver-haired bat (*Lasionycteris noctivagans*) for weeks before ovulation. In the California leaf-nosed bat (*Macrotus californicus*), the embryo implants in the

World primates, and elephant-shrews may reproduce at any time of the year. If the egg is not fertilized within a few days after ovulation, the uterus is sloughed off, resulting in bleeding. Some species only ovulate when conditions are right: Ord's kangaroo rats (*Dipodomys ordii*), for instance, may skip a year of reproduction if rainfall is sparse. Several carnivores, some rodents and insectivores, and

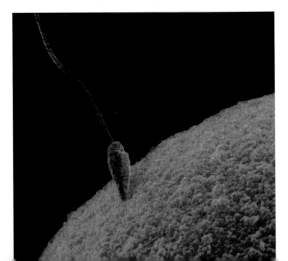

Sperm begin life in testes, which usually reside in a sac or scrotum outside the abdomen, but are sometimes inside, as in the case of the platypus and the elephant. No matter where they start, sperm look and move very much the same as they travel toward the egg, powered by their long tail, or flagella.

A female antechinus (right) lies in her nest, surrounded by her altricial young. Eight weeks earlier, when they first attached themselves to her teats, they were no bigger than grains of rice.

A female common zebra (Equus burchelli) nuzzles her newborn foal (below). Zebras—like many other ungulates, cetaceans, hyraxes, and some rodents—give birth to precocial young, meaning the young are able to walk, see, hear, and thermoregulate themselves.

The kangaroo-like Tammar wallaby (Macropus eugenii) (above) weighs only about 0.01 ounce (0.3 g) at birth. After a twenty-eight-day gestation, it makes its way from the vagina to the marsupium, where it nurses for the next eight to nine months. In some cases, while the joey is nursing, the mother is also carrying an embryo, conceived immediately after the joey's birth; the embryo remains dormant in the uterus until the joey stops nursing, at which point the embryo resumes development.

uterus wall and may wait several months before full-speed development begins. In bears and pinnipeds, the blastocyst (early embryo) may float in the uterus for weeks before implantation occurs. The delays serve various functions, mediating between sexual cycles of the different genders and ensuring that the young are born at the best possible time. Such needs are acute for mammals living in seasonally varying climates both near and far from the equator. Those that do not have reproductive delays tend to time mating so that gestation ends when weather is warm and food plentiful.

GESTATION

In general, the larger the placental mammal, the longer the gestation

Sperm Competition

A silverback gorilla keeps a harem of females for mating. His size and strength deter other males. But not all mammals compete this way for exclusive mating, nor are females usually monogamous. Some species of primates may mate with more than four partners a day while in heat. Against such promiscuity, males have various strategies to improve their chances of reproducing. Chemicals

instructions issued by various glands, the ovaries, and the embryo. Labor renders the placental female vulnerable to attack, so most births occur under the cover of night or early in the morning. Some will even cease labor during daylight and continue again at nightfall.

For marsupials and monotremes, labor is fairly routine. In both, the fertilized eggs do not implant into the uterus walls. The monotreme's eggs are soft-shelled, like those of a reptile. Glands in the uterus, which other mammals have lost through evolution, produce the shell. After a platypus lays her pair of eggs, she will curl up around them, incubating them for twelve days. With a special early tooth, the young peck their way free.

The marsupial embryo develops in a delicate yolk sac, which in some cases will attach itself to the uterine wall and be nourished for the length of the estrus cycle. Then it is ejected as a minimally developed neonatal animal and a new egg takes its place, ready for fertilization. When an eastern gray kangaroo (*Macropus giganteus*) joey is born, it is altricial—that is, it is totally helpless. It looks much like a worm with tiny front limbs. Instinctively it moves upward toward the teats in the marsupium, only six inches (15 cm) away. The mother assumes a curled-over posture for birth. As she licks her fur, she inadvertently makes a path for the newborn. The joey needs several minutes to find its way to a teat. Once it does, it latches on and remains there for three hundred days.

and the fewer the offspring. The blue whale—largest of all mammals—gestates a single fetus for about forty-eight weeks. During the last eight weeks, the fetal whale grows by more than two hundred pounds (90 kg) per day. At the other extreme, a western harvest mouse (*Reithrodontomys megalotis*) may gestate for only twenty-three days or so before producing a litter of up to nine young.

Birth and lactation are triggered by a complex feedback of hormonal

manufactured by a male ground squirrel seal up the vagina of his mate, though persistent competitors can pry loose the plug. Often competition for reproduction is tipped in favor of those who produce the most sperm, flooding out the competition. For example, the promiscuity of the female right whale is offset by the male's half-ton testes, which are five times bigger than those of the more exclusive, yet much larger, blue whale.

SENSES TO LIVE BY

A convoluted mantle of gray matter, the brain's neocortex receives sensory stimuli and is the site where much of the mammal's motor activity originates.

In the course of evolution, much of the ancestral brain that was devoted to olfactory stimuli has been transformed in mammals into other brain structures. Ultimately this has led to a substantial increase in brain size. In particular, the brain of mammals is distinguished by having a highly developed neocortex—an eighth-inch (3-mm) -thick, intricately folded layer of nerve cells devoted in part to interpreting sensory stimuli and initiating motor activity. This gray matter overlays the paleocortex, the primitive vertebrate brain, which controls vital functions such as mating and respiration.

The size and weight of a mammalian brain is not a true measure of intelligence—whales and elephants clearly have larger brains than man or any of the other primates. The amount of convolutions, however, is linked to intelligence, there being a great many more neuronal con-

"I could while away the hours,
Conferrin' with the flowers,
Consultin' with the rain,
And my head I'd be scratchin',
While my thoughts were
busy hatchin',
If I only had a brain."

— E.Y. HARBURG © COLUMBIA MUSIC

nections possible in a heavily convoluted surface area. For example, the neocortex of a chimpanzee is highly convoluted compared to that of a hedgehog, which is quite smooth.

Sensory stimuli are relayed by neurons to the neocortex as speedy electrochemical impulses. The endocrine system, moderated by the pituitary gland at the base of the brain, also sends messages to the sensory areas, but these are slower, longer-lasting, and transmitted

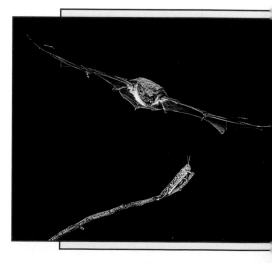

Senses and the Neocortex

The size of the area of the neocortex that is devoted to a particular sense tends to reflect the importance of that sense to the animal. For example, monkeys rely on sight rather than hearing to find food and defend themselves against attack, so the part of their neocortex devoted to vision is substantial.

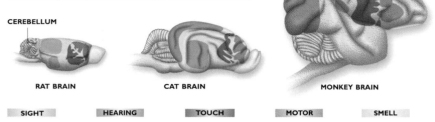

CEREBELLUM

RAT BRAIN   **CAT BRAIN**   **MONKEY BRAIN**

| SIGHT | HEARING | TOUCH | MOTOR | SMELL |

through the blood via chemicals called hormones.

The sizes of the areas devoted to motor activity and to receiving sensory stimuli vary from species to species, reflecting their relative importance to the mammal. The areas corresponding to touch *(page 53)* and motor activity are located side by side in the motor cortex, an area that is expanded in mammals such as primates, which depend on fine motor control. Also highly developed in mammals is the cerebellum, the section of the brain

that coordinates motion, balance, and posture.

Most mammals have excellent eyesight *(page 46)*, with all kinds of information—from shape and color to distance and motion—being simultaneously interpreted in various specialized areas of the visual cortex. Hearing *(page 48)*, another highly developed sense in mammals, is of particular importance to the 20 percent that rely on it instead of vision to find food and defend themselves. Sound is interpreted in the right and left halves of the auditory cortex, located near the ears.

The neurons transmitting information about smell *(page 50)* synapse first in the olfactory lobe. Then the information is relayed to the neocortex—only in smell is the neocortex the first stop in the neurosensory pathway—before traveling to several brain centers, including the limbic system, a part of the brain that plays a key role in memory. Taste *(page 52)*, an associated sense, is first detected by buds on the tongue and then transmitted to the brainstem. En route, neurons veer off to the limbic system as well.

Echolocation

Whether visually deficient or forced to find food or shelter under low-light conditions, mammals such as some bats, toothed whales, porpoises, and some shrews and tenrecs use high-frequency sound waves to echolocate during pursuit of prey. By comparing their emitted sound pulses to the returning echoes and analyzing the time lapse and difference in sound amplitude and frequency between the two, these mammals can build an aurally-based map of their surroundings and target their prey precisely.

Eyes to See With

The eyes of the least weasel (Mustela nivalis) shine blue-green in the dark.

The lens of the vertebrate eye focuses incoming light onto the retina lining the eye, where two different cells—called rods and cones because of their shapes—distinguish light levels and identify color, respectively. While a cone-poor retina is probably the ancestral mammalian condition, all mammals have some cones in their retinas, thus some capacity for color vision. But only primates, including some New World monkeys, Old World monkeys, and humans, have trichromatic vision, allowing them to detect the red, green, and blue portions of the spectrum.

The retinas of some diurnal mammals, such as squirrels, along with those of reptiles and birds, are almost completely packed with cones. Resulting acuity and color vision may be strong, but night vision suffers from lack of rods. Nocturnal animals with retinas that rely mostly on rods see principally in monochrome.

In rats and mice, rods and cones are distributed all over the retina, but in general these photosensitive cells tend to predominate in one area or another. In mammals the cones are concentrated in the fovea, located in the center of the retina. Many of these cones have a one-to-one connection with nerve fibers transmitting impulses to the optic nerve and the brain, and thus the fovea offers the greatest acuity. The fovea of mammals that live in forests and other habitats with contrasting elements is a circular structure, whereas that of mammals that live in grasslands and savannas, such as cheetahs and gazelles, tends to be an elongated strip, which allows for a wider focus area.

When light enters the eyes of nocturnal mammals, it stimulates the rods, then bounces off a reflecting membrane, the tapetum, behind the retina. Some light bounces back, giving the rods a second chance to absorb the rays. This membrane is responsible for the eye-shine of animals caught in headlights. Retinal pigments—and therefore the color they reflect—differ across species. For example, deer reflect white light, whereas lynx and other cats reflect gold, skunks amber, raccoons yellow, and opossums and bears various shades of orange or red.

BINOCULAR VISION

Many mammals have front-facing eyes, a sign of true predators. Binocular vision from the overlap of the fields of vision of each eye, along with the depth and distance perception this affords, help canids and felines to scope out and chase prey. Animals such as snowshoe

hares that are frequent prey have eyes closer to the sides of the head and are more reliant on peripheral vision; many can scan the full 360-degree visual range for danger without moving their head or rolling their eyes.

Visual Communication

Social diurnal mammals often use elaborate visual signals to communicate. Whether between or within species, these cues indicate whether the animal should be approached or feared. Examples of visual signals include:

• Color displays: The females of many primate species display genital swelling and flushing to indicate sexual responsiveness.

• Piloerection: Cats signal fear and threat by arching their back and raising the hair on their nape and tail.

• Pinned-back ears: Dogs, horses, bats, cats, bears, raccoons, and antelopes draw back their ears when signaling submissiveness or aggression.

• Facial expressions: Many primates communicate with their face. Diurnal monkeys, for instance, signal aggression by narrowing their eyes.

• Body language: Some ungulates use their entire body to indicate threat. For example, the ibex rears up on its hindlegs and the African buffalo circles its opponent, displaying a full side view of its formidable body.

A bobcat (Lynx rufus) chases a snowshoe hare (Lepus americanus) through the snow in the foothills of the Colorado Rockies. Although the bobcat's forward-facing eyes restrict its field of view to about 187 degrees, the consequent overlap increases visual definition and depth perception.

Ears for Hearing

The large pinnae of the fennec fox (Vulpes zerda) help it to capture the subtle sounds of nightlife on the North African desert.

Air transmits sound waves less efficiently than water, so when the distant ancestors of mammals moved onto land, modifications were needed to help catch and amplify the weakened vibrations.

Most mammals have pinnae—exterior ears—for gathering and funneling sound inward. From there, the sound travels along a canal to the ear drum. The resonance of this pipelike ear canal, or auditory meatus, serves to amplify sound, almost doubling its force. When sound waves hit the taut membrane of the ear drum at the far end, they are converted to mechanical vibrations, which are then transferred to the malleus, the incus, and the stapes, the tiny bones that make up the middle ear. These bones, or ossicles, work together—the malleus pushes the incus, which pushes the stapes—doubling or tripling the force of vibration in the process. Last in line, the stapes exerts pressure on the so-called oval window, a membrane covering the opening of the inner ear, a fluid-filled, spiral-shaped structure known as the cochlea. The concentration of force that occurs as the vibrations pass from the ear drum to the much smaller oval window produces an additional fifteen- to thirtyfold amplification. At this point, the vibrations are converted into hydraulic pressure waves that pass through the liquid of the inner ear, ultimately stimulating the nerve endings that generate electrical impulses to the brain.

Not surprisingly, the mammalian ear—an organ designed to transduce sound traveling from air to fluid—doesn't work as well under water. Thus, marine mammals have had to make their own modifications. Cetaceans, for instance, have small holes located just behind their eyes instead of pinnae—which would obstruct the smooth passage of water along their streamlined body. In an additional adaptation, their middle and inner ears are suspended by ligaments, isolating them from their skull, which, along with their body, absorbs sound from the water and therefore would interfere with sound reception in

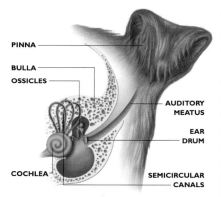

PINNA

BULLA

OSSICLES

AUDITORY
MEATUS

EAR
DRUM

COCHLEA

SEMICIRCULAR
CANALS

The Mammalian Ear
*One of the main features of the mammalian ear
is the bulla, a bone that houses and protects the
ossicles of the middle ear while also enhancing
the conduction of low-frequency sound.*

the inner ear. Sound is transmitted
to their inner ear along a fat deposit
running the length of the lower jaw.

The frequency of sound is measured in cycles per second. Most
mammals can hear a much wider
range of sound frequency than they
can produce. A dog, for example,
can perceive frequencies between
15 and 50,000 cycles, but makes
sounds only within the range of
452 to 1,080 cycles.

The hearing range of a mammal
tends to correspond to its survival
needs. For instance, although
smaller mammals generally hear
and emit sounds at higher frequencies than larger animals, the
enlarged bulla of the tiny desert
kangaroo rat (*Dipodomys deserti*)
increases its sensitivity to low
frequencies, thus allowing it to
perceive the low-intensity, low-
frequency sounds made by predators, including the sidewinder rattlesnake and the barn owl. Other
rodents living in dry environments,
such as the lesser Egyptian jerboa
(page 139), also exhibit this
increased sensitivity, leading some
researchers to believe that the adaptation may also have developed as
compensation for the poor sound-
carrying quality of dry desert air.

Mammal Talk

Auditory communication is almost
universal among mammals, and
can include non-vocal as well as vocal
sounds. The mountain gorillas, for
instance, beat their chest with cupped
hands to intimidate enemies, while
banner-tail kangaroo rats make the
ground vibrate when they drum it
with their hind feet to mark territory,
compete for mates, or distinguish
friend from foe. Vocal style may also
be distinct for each individual. For
example, Southeast Asian gibbons can
identify the sex of a caller, their family,
and ultimately individual identity. Calls
typically indicate:
• Dominance and submission: Primates
and carnivores often use sound to
signal who's in and who's out. For
example, squirrel monkeys have a
repertoire of growls and grunts to
indicate social status within the group.
• Alarm: Many primates signal alarm
with their cries. Vervet monkeys
even have a range of different alarm
shrieks to indicate particular types
of predators.
• Territoriality: North American
woodchucks use high-pitched
squeaks and whistles to signal when
their territory is being invaded.
• Mating: Some mammal species
employ sound as they court. For
example, Asian elephants emit
infrasound rumblings to indicate
reproductive receptivity.

Smell, Taste, & Touch

The sense of smell plays a crucial role in the daily lives of most mammals, from helping them find and test the edibility of food to detecting and identifying friends, foes, prey, and suitable sexual partners.

OLFACTORY EQUIPMENT

The ability of mammals to smell depends on a relay system made up of receptor cells, nerves, and the olfactory lobe, a structure found in the anterior portion of the brain that is responsible for the collection and analysis of scent molecules prior to the journey to the neocortex and various brain centers.

The receptor cells are concentrated in a pair of olfactory clefts located just above the air passages in each nasal chamber of the nose. The clefts are lined with a complex network of small scroll-like bones, called turbinates, and a membrane of yellowish epithelium that is composed of millions of receptor cells. These cells pick up strong scents as the mammal breathes. Weaker scents are purposefully drawn into the nose and over the receptors by sniffing.

The larger the surface area of the nose's epithelium—and therefore the more scent receptors—the better a mammal's sense of smell will be. Dogs, for example, have more than 250 million receptors in an area of membrane about fifty times bigger than that found in humans, who are served by about five million receptors.

Olfactory Lobes

The importance of smell in a mammal's life is reflected by the size of its olfactory lobe. The aardvark, for instance, needs strong scenting abilities to detect the termites it feeds on. The chimpanzee, on the other hand, relies on its excellent vision to find food, so the olfactory part of its brain is relatively small.

OLFACTORY LOBE

Brain of an Aardvark

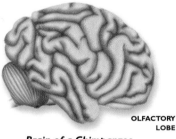

OLFACTORY LOBE

Brain of a Chimpanzee

The olfactory system is most highly developed, of course, in mammals that rely mainly on it to stay alive, such as nocturnal insectivores, carnivores, and rodents. Humans and other higher primates have more poorly developed olfactory systems. Essentially diurnal, they depend on their superior vision to find food and to detect both prey and predators. Most cetaceans have very few olfactory receptors and appear to have lost their sense of smell. Baleen whales, however, have more olfactory receptors than toothed whales and may "sniff" the air with their blowhole when they surface to smell for plankton-rich waters.

Apart from its value in seeking the food they need to survive, mammals use their sense of smell to communicate. They manufacture volatile chemical signals, called pheromones, and excrete them along with feces and urine or emit them from scent glands located in various places on their body. These personal messages are left sometimes deliberately, sometimes unknowingly. Often one sniff is all the receiver needs in order to determine age, gender, health, and sexual and social status of the sender.

Scent Glands

The violet areas indicate scent glands on a mule deer. Those below the eyes release secretions that are rubbed on twigs. Secretions from glands around the anus mark the deer's feces, while those from glands on the tail and legs transmit scent through the air and also mark grass and brush as the deer travels about. Interdigital glands between the deer's hooves scent-mark the ground it walks on. During the rut, bucks reinforce the scent from the tuft of hair on their hocks—known as the tarsal gland—by deliberately urinating on them.

TERRITORIAL MARKERS

Canids such as wolves and coyotes deposit urine and feces in key spots around their territory as "Keep Out" signs for potential intruders.

They will also leave pheromone-rich markers to alert themselves that they are back on their own turf after returning from a trip beyond.

To advertise sexual availability, some mammals, such as male rhinoceroses, stamp on or roll in their own urine. Similarly, camels mark their legs by swishing their tail while urinating. Male wapiti urinate directly on their belly and billy goats ejaculate into their

The gray wolf (Canis lupus) uses scent not only for marking territory, but also as a prelude to mating. Here, a male gray wolf sniffs at the anal glands of a female to gauge her sexual receptiveness.

beard—all in the name of sexual attractiveness.

Mammalian scent glands are located around the mouth, eyes, paws, sex organ, anus, and elsewhere. Domestic cats use the glands on their cheeks to mark trees, furniture, and the pant legs of their favorite humans. Both wild and domestic felines have glands in their foot pads, leaving behind pheromone-rich scents when scratching objects to sharpen their claws. Many hoofed mammals, including deer and caribou, have interdigital glands located between their hooves and leave a scent trail on the ground they walk over. Hyraxes and capybaras are alone in having scent glands on the skin of their back. Pigs have them on their knees.

GAPE, GRIN, AND GRIMACE

Some mammals possess a lesser known piece of olfactory equipment known as the vomeronasal, or Jacobson's (after its discoverer), organ. The organ is a small, pouch-like opening located in the roof of the mouth near the nasal palate of such mammals as felines, ungulates, and some canines. After detecting certain scents, a mammal equipped with this organ can block off its normal breathing channels and draw air into the pouch through an odd combination of gape, grin, and grimace, known as the flehmen response—almost as if it were actually tasting the air. The flehmen response is typically employed by mammals to analyze the urine of others of their kind, particularly by males seeking to determine the sexual status of females. Domestic-cat owners may well recognize this technique since cats occasionally flehmen in response to the smells left behind by another cat.

TASTE

Most mammals, including humans, have a far better sense of smell than of taste. In fact, smell helps refine taste. Cold sufferers know that their ability to taste is seriously diminished by a blocked nose. Like scent, taste involves the detection of chemicals, but ones found in solids and fluids, not in the air. Groups of taste receptors, known as taste buds, are spread over the tongue. Humans have about nine thousand taste buds on their tongue and can detect five

Rat Brain

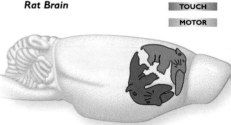

TOUCH

MOTOR

Ratunculus
The brain areas devoted to touch and motor activity are represented in the neocortex by distorted maps of the mammal in question. Called the homunculus, meaning "little man," in humans and ratunculus in rats such as the black rat (Rattus rattus) shown at right, each map reflects the importance of the roles played by different parts of the mammal's body. In the example above, clearly the snout and whiskers are vital to the rat's ability to sense its environment.

basic tastes: salty, sour, sweet, bitter, and glutamate. A canid tongue has only about two thousand taste buds.

Unlike scent receptors, the pear-shaped taste buds of mammals are not connected directly to the brain. They rely on indirect nerve links to carry their messages. The cells that cluster to form taste buds are short-lived. Most die after about seven to ten days, while others last a mere twenty-four hours. New taste cells are continually replacing dying ones.

TOUCH

Touch receptors, often called mechanoreceptors, are also being continually replaced in the skin's epidermis. These cells, which con-sist of nerve-fiber terminals embed-ded in the skin, undergo electro-chemical changes whenever their membranes are deformed, resulting in the transmission of informa-tion about pressure to the brain. Each type responds to a par-ticular kind of pressure. For

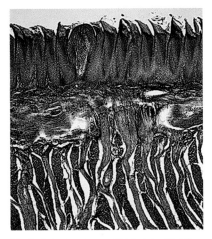

The bulb in the top row of pink-stained papillae on this rabbit's tongue is a taste bud. Formed by the clustering of taste cells, these buds act as receptors for detecting flavor molecules in food and fluids.

example, Merkel corpuscles are cells that react to changing defor-mation of the skin and Meissner corpuscles react to a steady pressure on the skin.

As well as touch receptor cells, most mammals have at least some form of whiskers, or vibrissae, on their body that serve to extend a mammal's touch capabilities beyond its epidermis. Long, stiff, modified hairs, vibrissae are typical-ly found on the face and muzzle and lower legs. Nocturnal mammals use them to help navigate in the dark. The whiskers of felines are said to pick up the slightest varia-tion in air currents and those of various aquatic mammals can detect subtle changes in water currents as well as the pres-ence of anything moving, such as fish, in dark waters.

Mammal Minds

One day at Marineland in Florida, an older dolphin named Zippy was observed moving found items—pens, coins, and the like accidentally dropped into the marine pool—out of the way of cleanup divers, then secreting them in an area the cleanup crew had already swept. Was this some instinctive ritual or was it an example of a wily intelligence at work?

The notion that non-human mammals possess some power of reasoning has long had the power to stir controversy. While it is widely accepted today that all mammals share certain physiological and behavioral characteristics, there is still no consensus on the extent—or even the nature—of mammalian intelligence.

Studies have provided evidence that mammals are capable of recognizing patterns, gathering and integrating information, and solving problems. But because assessments of animal intelligence have relied so extensively on human intelligence as the benchmark, much research has been debunked as anthropomorphism—the ascribing of human attributes and characteristics to non-humans. Another criticism is that intelligence research has focused too heavily on animals in captivity, out of their natural environments.

MONKEY SEE, MONKEY SAY?

Because of their genetic similarity to humans, primates have been obvious candidates for intelligence research

An African elephant, in what is believed by some researchers to be a typical response to the death of a companion, prods the corpse of another, killed and mutilated by poachers. After prodding the corpse, the elephant is likely to circle the body, then stand facing outward, its trunk hanging limply to the ground. This oft-repeated behavior, as well as the profound interest displayed by elephants in the bones of dead elephants—they will examine them at length, smell them, even carry them a distance—has provoked speculation that elephants may have some concept of death.

Although dolphins have been shown to be capable of following and interpreting sets of instructions, there is no evidence that they employ anything resembling language in the wild.

studies. And since language is considered by many to be a measure of intelligence, much attention has centered on whether apes could be taught to communicate in human languages.

Washoe, a female chimpanzee, has learned to use more than a hundred signs derived from American Sign Language (ASL), gestures developed for communication by the deaf. While on a boat ride with her trainers in the early 1970s, she saw a swan for the first time. Having no sign in her vocabulary for such a thing, she signed "waterbird."

A celebrated gorilla named Koko started sign language training more than twenty years ago. After two months of instruction, she could string words together, signing simple phrases such as "more food" and "more drink more." One month later, she was requesting specific games. In 1998 Koko became the first non-human to appear live on the Internet, answering questions about her life and desires.

CONSCIOUSNESS CONTROVERSY

Research on animal intelligence has prompted much speculation about their possible consciousness. An elusive concept to define, consciousness is sometimes said to reveal itself in three ways: language; self-awareness; and awareness that others also have minds.

Ongoing research by Scottish and German zoologists on chimpanzees located at centers scattered across Africa suggests that they display behavioral "complexes" that are neither genetically nor environmentally derived. Instead, they appear to have been culturally transmitted, the result of the chimpanzees copying one another. Termite fishing with twigs and the midribs of leaves are two examples. Another is the breaking open of nuts with a hammer—done in four different ways, each having its own occurrence pattern at different sites. Does evidence of cultures among chimpanzees suggest consciousness? The debate continues and may never be completely decided. But as scientist Stephen Walker wrote, "Our organ of thought may be superior, and we may play it better, but it is surely vain to believe that other possessors of similar instruments leave them quite untouched."

SOCIAL BEHAVIOR

Along with environmental and genetic factors, social forces shape behavior, and all contribute to the survival of the species.

Propagation of genes is the primary objective of life; thus, parental behaviors that promote the survival of offspring are at the heart of all socially relevant conduct.

"Besides love and sympathy, animals exhibit other qualities connected with the social instincts which in us would be called moral."

— CHARLES ROBERT DARWIN

mated 95 percent of mammal species are reared solely by their mothers. The period of intimacy between mother and young, though, varies according to species and circumstance. Elephant calves, for instance, are dependent on mother's care for the first dozen years or so; the hooded seal (*Cystophora cristata*), however, weans her pup in four days.

Mammals are born helpless to some degree or another, and none would survive very long without the instinct to nurse. For some mammals, this involves more than the instinct to root and suck. Bear cubs, for instance, know enough to hum as they nurse to stimulate milk production by their hibernating mother.

Parenting may be instinctual, too, affected by brain hormones *(box, page opposite)*, although learning also plays a role. Because mammalian females nurse their young, they are well-adapted for child care; an esti-

The male of some species aids the mother in early parenting. The male black-backed jackal (*Canis mesomalis*), for example, hunts and fetches food while the female is den-bound with cubs. The couple then rears the cubs together, and mature offspring often stay with the family to help with their parents' next litter.

Many mammal mothers care for their

Like many grassland ungulates, blue gnus (Connochaetes taurinus) are nomadic grazers that travel in large herds. The herds become stationary during breeding season, when the males set up territories and establish harems. After weaning, male offspring join hierarchical bachelor herds, while mother and daughters stay together for two or three years.

young within the safety of a group. One such group is the cohesive herd typified by some large ungulates. Their very size renders them visible and vulnerable on the grasslands where they live. While young or weakened stragglers are easy targets for predators, so too are those that are more individualistic. Thus, herding behavior becomes reinforced through natural selection. Group life also tends to occur when rich food sources are widely scattered, as is the case of the savanna baboon, which is more likely to find food the greater the number of foragers involved in the search.

When food is hard to come by, mammals are often solitary. Land carnivores such as the large cats and bears spend the majority of their adult life hunting and foraging alone, marking and defending their territory *(page 61)*—only coming together to mate. Conversely, although food is rarely scarce for insectivores, they too are frequently solitary, using olfactory and perhaps acoustical signals to attract mates. Exceptions include those insectivores, such as several shrew species, that share the same nest, presumably for warmth.

Two adult Japanese macaques (Macaca fuscata) huddle for warmth around a young monkey in the mountains of northern Honshu. Like most primates, macaques are social creatures. This species, however, is also matrilineal, meaning the social status of the young depends on the rank of the mother.

A Chemical Bond

Recent studies of rodents, sheep, and monkeys suggest that some hormones promote good parenting skills, particularly among social mammals. Oxytocin, linked mostly with childbirth and lactation (although present in both sexes), and the structurally similar hormone vasopressin, linked with heightened territoriality in males, both seem to influence sexual and postpartum behavior. In one study, a connection was found between these hormones and increased frequency of mating behavior; cuddling between mother and child; and nest-building and infant-caring behavior in fathers. Moreover, when the hormones' actions were blocked in rats, males became violent with offspring and females became less receptive to male advances.

Play

Play is loosely defined by scientists as vigorous movements performed by the young for no immediate benefit, but which often have counterparts in serious adult behavior. Play may be solitary, as in the studying of and pouncing on a swaying blade of grass by a leopard cub, or social, as when wolf pack-mates romp and nip at one another. It is a common activity among most mammals, especially those most intelligent and social, such as primates, dolphins, and carnivores. Invertebrates, fish, and reptiles lack play behavior, but it has been observed among birds such as ravens.

Play requires huge amounts of extra energy and it cuts into food-gathering time. Furthermore, it often exposes the young to predators while at the same time involving potentially dangerous activities. Despite its high costs, mammals continue to play in part because it teaches them essential skills for survival. For example, young gibbons swing from branches—a critical adult skill—even after falling to the forest floor.

Sometimes play enables adults to display better parenting skills. Monkeys and apes, for instance, show more attention and patience with their offspring when they have had experience as juveniles playing with their younger siblings.

Social play-fighting is characterized by frequent body contact, rapid role reversal from "predator" to "prey," and exaggerations of everyday adult behavior. Mammals that are frequently food for predators play at escaping. Even ungulates and large herbivores, such as antelopes, which rarely play, practice these maneuvers.

Play partners differ from species to species. Some young play only with their own gender, and consequently there may be great differ-

More aggressive in their play than either young dogs or wolves, young coyotes (Canis latrans) typically play with each other only after they've established which one is top dog.

ences in play between males and females. For example, male Steller sea lions (*Eumetopias jubatus*) bite when they play, but the females do not, preferring calmer activities.

While play-wrestling promotes brain and physical development, young mammals such as these chimpanzees do it for the fun.

Shared play is believed by some mammalogists to build and strengthen social bonds. If this is so, however, they are at a loss to explain why mammals of different species sometimes play together. Baboons have been observed playing with their chimpanzee predators as have jackals with Thomson's gazelles, to cite only a few examples. Furthermore, if play is designed to promote social bonds, one might expect a correlation between play and sociability. But several species, including the American black bear and the tiger quoll (*Dasyurus maculatus*), that play vigorous and elaborate games as cubs are solitary as adults.

LET'S PLAY

The young of many species use "play faces" to indicate they want to engage in only pretend activity, probably to stay out of trouble since play often resembles adult behavior—superficially. Employed by most mammals, especially primates and carnivores, the standard play-face is a wide-open mouth. Chimpanzees modify this face with lips drawn over their teeth. Other variations on the "let's play" signal include mongooses whipping their tail, badgers performing head twists, and dogs bowing—crouching down with their rear held high.

With parent-child play, the young have a safe forum to learn. To teach fox kits the goal of the hunt, adults bring disabled prey back for their young to play with. The play may be gentle, as with gorilla mothers playing peek-a-boo, or rough, as when lion cubs bite their mother.

Play stimulates the brain as well as the body. Especially in intelligent mammals, new synaptic connections in the brain's cerebellum are formed, old ones are reinforced, and some are rewired according to experience. For some mammals, the period during which this center for balance, coordination, and muscle control is remodeled coincides with the ages at which juveniles play the most. In large-brained species such as primates and dolphins, the longer periods of postnatal brain development coincide with extended and intense play phases.

Social Hierarchy

Whether at home or traveling to new territory, mammal groups maintain order with the help of a social hierarchy, referred to by mammalogists as a dominance hierarchy. The rules of conduct that it implies help determine outcomes to issues important to the group, especially which one gets to breed and which one gets to eat first. Dominance hierarchies are headed by a single male (usually) or female, by a dominant pair, or by a dominant group.

The result of dominance hierarchies is to limit violence within the group, and such is the consequence whether the hierarchy is a simple pecking order or a complicated interaction of dominance networks and bargaining strategies. A typical dominance hierarchy includes an alpha male or pair of males that are the sole breeders within the group. Beta males act as second-in-command, cooperating with alphas, whereas lower-rung males, sometimes referred to as deltas and gammas, will periodically try to compete for increased stature.

Hierarchies are maintained even when groups migrate to new areas. In the bands formed by hamadryas baboons (*Papio hamadryas*), which are made up of smaller breeding units, or harems, the male harem leaders join forces to set the direction in which the entire troop moves. By contrast, the alpha male stag circling a herd of female Eurasian red deer (*Cervus elaphus*) follows wherever the females decide to go. His job basically is to herd stray females back to the group.

Dominant males rarely kill within their group. However, struggles are common. Also common are calls and displays: The dominant South American red howler monkey (*Alouatta seniculus*) howls the loudest with his low bass voice, while the dominant Australian sugar glider (*Petaurus breviceps*) secretes more copiously from his scent gland than do the other males.

Giraffe bulls sometimes engage in mock battles to test each other's strength and therefore status within the dominance hierarchy that defines their herd. The outcome of such "necking" will help to determine which bull gains access to the cows.

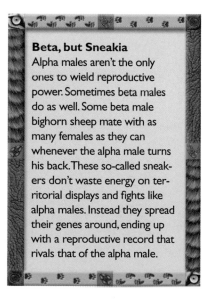

Male red kangaroos spar to establish their position in the "mob," a term Australians use for a kangaroo group.

there is a threat display, most notably a sudden increase in the apparent size of the individual. If no one backs down, the competitors mimic movements like those of an attack. This can then progress to a tame ritual fight. If things escalate, the actual fight is often brief and intense, with the loser running off and the winner standing ground on his territory.

Female-dominated territories are sometimes more hard-won and defended. Related female Belding's ground squirrels (*Spermophilus beldingi*) will cooperate in defense of their neighboring burrows. And lone European rabbit (*Oryctolagus cuniculus*) females, for instance, fight to the death for possession of their burrows.

Female displays of dominance are also seen in competitions for a male or for territory. Sometimes, however, females cooperate to get what they want, as in the case of female yellow baboons (*Papio cynocephalus*). Working together, several females harass other females in the harem into suppressing their ovulation—a surefire technique to ensure their own reproductive dominance.

In territorial systems, the available space is split up. At the start of the breeding season, males establish their space by various means, including sound, such as the bugling of the male Eurasian red deer, and scent markings *(page 51)*.

Male-dominated territories often have well-defined centers, but their somewhat blurred boundaries inspire ownership challenges. First,

Beta, but Sneakia
Alpha males aren't the only ones to wield reproductive power. Sometimes beta males do as well. Some beta male bighorn sheep mate with as many females as they can whenever the alpha male turns his back. These so-called sneakers don't waste energy on territorial displays and fights like alpha males. Instead they spread their genes around, ending up with a reproductive record that rivals that of the alpha male.

Making Nice

One of the few scientific concepts to enter the popular lexicon is "survival of the fittest." A basic tenet of modern evolutionary theory, it is linked to the concept of natural selection *(page 31)*, which holds that the fittest members of a species population are the ones that survive and reproduce. While most people today agree that animals are driven to compete ruthlessly in order to stay alive, some would also argue that these same ruthless animals are also capable of altruism.

FAMILY TIES

Marmosets search for food as a family and share it—often right out of each other's mouth. Older siblings act as surrogate parents, feeding, carrying, teaching, and protecting the babies. According to one theory, these acts are the basis of a type of natural selection called kin selection, a mechanism whereby an individual increases the survival opportunities and reproductive success—the "fitness"—of siblings or cousins as well as offspring, thus helping to ensure that its own genes will get passed on. Such inclusive fitness, as the behavior is called, also results in an increase of the genes for altruistic behavior in the population.

KIND NEIGHBORS

Some mammals have been observed being kind to unrelated animals. Called reciprocal altruism, this behavior is less common than kin selection and it can evolve only if the kind-doer eventually reaps some future benefit. This means that animals must be able to distinguish among individuals in the group and remember who helped whom and when. A classic example involves vampire bats (*Desmodus rotundus*), which build alliances by sharing food. They fly from their roosts at night to feed on the blood of cattle and horses. Because those that do not find nourishment will

Recent studies carried out among free-ranging horses of the Camargue in the south of France have shown that there is a survival benefit to cooperation: Foals born into a group controlled by cooperating males were seven times more likely to survive the early days of life than those born into a group dominated by a single high-ranking male. The males that forged cooperative bonds were also more likely to sire foals than those that didn't.

starve within two to three days, a fully-fed bat—typically after some persuasive grooming—may regurgitate some of what it has consumed and share it with a hungry roost-mate. This is considered reciprocal altruism because the hungry bat is very likely to return the favor by donating a meal at some later time.

Monkeys, baboons, and other mammals that groom each other are not simply cleaning the hair of dirt and parasites; they are building social bonds. In some cases, a grooming holds out the promise that in times of need—when under attack or needing help to fight off rivals when the time comes to mate—the groomer has allies to call on.

One of the more intriguing examples of altruistic behavior displayed by mammals involves the courting ritual of gray whales (*Eschrichtius robustus*), which

Monkeys such as the dusky titi (Callicebus moloch) shown here bond through grooming, cuddling, and tail-wrapping. These ties may reap life-saving benefits in times of need.

engages two males and one female. They swim together, playfully rubbing and rolling against each other, for five thousand miles (8,000 km) to the warm ocean waters off Baja. Lingering in the shallows, they brush increasingly harder against one another until the female indicates her choice by rolling toward one of the males. The spurned male then positions himself as a bulwark to support the female while his rival impregnates her. While it is not known whether there was any reciprocity involved, the males have never been seen to fight with each other.

In a highly influential book entitled *The Selfish Gene*, evolutionary biologist Richard Dawkins takes a gene-centered view of altruism, arguing that instead of organisms using genes to reproduce themselves, it is the genes that manipulate the body in which they ride. "The animal," he claims, "is a survival machine for its genes." If so, "selfish" genes have done a masterful job of crafting altruistic survival machines.

Courtship & Mating

In his breeding season, with miles of dark ocean often between him and a potential mate, the male humpback whale (*Megaptera novaeangliae*) cannot rely on an elaborate dance or colorful display to capture a female's attention. Instead, he sings a complicated but melodious underwater love song for up to thirty minutes to attract potential mates.

Male humpbacks aren't the only mammals that break into song during breeding season. During his courting ritual, the grasshopper mouse (*Onychomys leucogaster*), a carnivorous New World rodent, stands on his hindlegs and belts out a verse or two of an odd chirplike tune to attract females of his kind.

Female mammals also announce their sexual readiness, but often indirectly through chemical messages *(page 51)*. When it comes to active courting, males usually take the lead. Some large ungulates, such as moose and wapiti, emit strong, musky scents and make throaty calls to broadcast their powerful desire to mate.

For social species that live in groups of both males and females, locating a mate poses no problem at all. The challenge for a male in these groups lies in convincing a female to choose him over other males. Many mammals engage in ritual fights with rivals for the right to mate with their group's female or females. Dominant male elephant seals and walruses are just a few of the species that must constantly fend off challenges from other males in order to maintain mating rights to the females in their harems.

TWO TO TANGO

Once a mate has been singled out, mammals may display one of a variety of courtship dances. Platypuses swim after each other

The elephant's version of foreplay often culminates in loud grunting and even trumpeting, but the sex act itself takes place in almost total silence.

Male lions can detect a female's estrus by smelling her urine. Copulation lasts for anywhere from five to twenty seconds and may be repeated every half hour for as long as a week.

in a tight circle, gently tugging at and nuzzling each other. Male elephants are affectionate, gentle, and surprisingly delicate with their favorite females during their long courtship. But when the female comes into season, both males and females become extremely passionate. The female will alternately tempt the male with caresses from her trunk and provocative body language, and then resist his advances before finally copulating.

Things can get a little rougher in other species. Dolphins often bite and scratch each other and rhinoceroses may gouge each other to the point of serious injury while copulating. In some primates, the entire sex act may last only seconds, while other species, such as black-footed ferrets (*Mustela nigripes*), may remained locked together for up to an hour. Some mammals mate only once; others favor serial copulation. Shaw's jird (*Meriones shawi*), a small African desert rodent, has been observed copulating 224 times in under two hours and a female baboon in heat was once recorded

as mating ninety-three times with three different partners over her five-day estrus. While insectivores, rodents, and bats tend to go their separate ways after copulating, in some species a close bond develops between the male and female that goes well beyond the estrus period. After a long courtship and subsequent mating, coyotes may pair-bond for years, sometimes even life. Monogamy is also practiced by the South American titi monkey *(page 62)*, although in this case it doesn't prevent the monogamous male from copulating with other females when an opportunity arises.

Stiff Competition

Since they give birth to only a single calf every four or five years, fertile female bottlenose dolphins are a rarity and competition among males for their attentions can be fierce. Male bottlenoses have been known to take unusual measures to copulate with them. Researchers have reported seeing groups of two or three males enlist the aid of another group to violently attack a third group containing a female and squire her away. Although they have been spotted sniffing around the female bottlenose's genitalia, it is not known if or how males detect sexual receptiveness in females. If she isn't ovulating, they may simply try and keep her around until she is.

BACKYARD
& BEYOND

MAMMAL WATCHING

*Learn to understand mammals by practicing
the art of patient observation.*

COMPASS

BINOCULARS

GLOBAL
POSITIONING
SYSTEM

SPOTTING
SCOPE

Avoid getting lost in the wild by taking a map of the region, a compass, and, if it's an extensive wilderness area, a global positioning system (GPS). This device picks up signals of satellites to help pinpoint your position anywhere on Earth. For seeing wildlife up close, binoculars are a must; to view distant mammals, such as caribou traveling across the tundra, also take a spotting scope, which can be set up on a portable tripod. At night, cover your flashlight with a red filter or red cellophane to avoid alarming animals. Before starting out, listen to the weather forecast.

Most wild mammals are secretive and shy; their survival depends on being cautious and staying hidden from predators—including humans. Some of them, however, can be lured close enough to be seen from a back porch. If you can hang a bird feeder at the far end of the garden, it will not only attract birds, but may also draw squirrels and raccoons. Or, set out a salt block for deer, porcupines, and other rodents to lick; they get salt-deprived, especially in the winter, and will suspend their timidity in order to replenish their salt reserves.

Drawing wild mammals close to home, however, has its drawbacks—not the least of which may be an invasion of your neighbor's yard as well. Also, once a mammal such as a raccoon has figured out that there are interesting food possibilities around your home, it will return again and again.

Nothing is more satisfying, of course, than observing wild mammals in their natural habitat. While there are few true wilderness areas left, many of the national parks, as well as state, provincial, and wildlife preserves, hold ample opportunities for seeing animals as they go about their daily life. Some of the best known parks and preserves are listed on pages 177 to 179.

Before you head out, consult the guide section of this book *(pages 82 to 174)* for information about some of the mammals you may see. Find out about the types of signs and tracks they leave behind *(pages 72 to 75)* and what behavior to watch for according to the season *(pages 76 to 79)*.

"Come forth into the light of things, Let Nature be your teacher"

— WILLIAM WORDSWORTH

WAITING AND WATCHING

Wildlife watchers need to develop patience and a keen eye. Take your time as you walk, stopping now and then to listen and look. Focus your listening: Sounds can be magnified to more than double their volume by cupping the hands behind the ears and pushing them out slightly as you face the noise. To see better, try a traditional North American aboriginal technique called "splatter vision." Unfocus your eyes to maximize your peripheral vision and increase your view to a nearly 180-degree field of vision. Ask yourself what doesn't fit in the scene around you: A strange black blob high in a poplar tree, for instance, may be a porcupine; a quick movement off to the side may be a deer. If you become aware of a wild creature in the vicinity, try to approach it slowly and quietly, if possible in an angled approach from downwind. If the mammal looks up, avoid staring and freeze in place until it resumes its activity. Often the animal will know that you're there; but looking away and holding still simply makes you appear less threatening.

Whale Watching

If you plan to join an ocean-going whale-watching expedition, keep an eye out for a series of misty blows, revealing the presence of whales. Approach slowly, staying at least three hundred feet (90 m) away at all times. If the boat gets too close, it may cause the whales to abandon what may be a rich feeding area. Avoid crowding the whales; there should be no more than two to three boats of observers nearby at any one time. Allow the whales to decide how long the interaction lasts; when they've had enough, they will swim away.

Urban Dwellers

Many mammals have been displaced by our buildings and streets, but some species have surfed the tidal wave of human progress and are now more numerous within city boundaries than in the countryside. The urban world offers them everything they need: a place to breed, nooks and crannies in which to hide, and many sources of food.

For in-town dining, it helps to be a generalist like the raccoon. These striped bandits are wizards at getting at food, easily unlatching screen doors, pulling open fridge doors, and slipping lids off garbage cans. They have adapted so well to city life that in one survey it was estimated that their urban population density was six times that just outside the same city.

King of the city-dwellers is the house rat—either *Rattus rattus*, the black rat, or *R. norvegicus*, the brown rat. Both these rats originated in the Old World, Asia probably, and today can be found in almost every North American city, living off refuse and thriving in the poorest areas. In the Middle Ages, house rats hosted the fleas that spread the Black Death, a plague that killed about one-quarter of Europe's population. House rats still harbor at least twenty diseases that can be transmitted to humans. And they are tough. They can even survive being flushed down a toilet; indeed *R.*

norvegicus can enter a building via this drainage route.

If house rats are the toughest city mammals, house mice are the most numerous. It is estimated that more than one billion house mice live in the United States alone, and they are probably second only to the house rat in destructiveness. Even so, both rodents have been of great benefit to humans. White laboratory rats, bred from their wild cousins, serve an invaluable purpose in medical and psychological experiments, which depend on some eighteen million rats a year to further scientific knowledge.

Cities near wilderness will naturally tend to see

Cities like Anchorage, Alaska, that are surrounded by wilderness attract less urbanized mammals such as this moose.

more than the usual number of wild mammals. Deer may be observed nibbling at fruit trees and foxes are spotted trotting along the street as they make their feeding rounds. The smallest bit of cover will lure rabbits to backyards, while woodchucks and pocket gophers make their own cover by digging burrows.

Raccoons are familiar city-dwellers, as are gray, red, and fox squirrels, which feed on nuts and seeds as well as discarded human food. Gray squirrels, in particular, are a common city sight, their leafy nests visible high in trees, especially after leaf-fall. Most gray squirrels are accurately described by their name, but in some areas they are black, blond, reddish, even albino. Porches and sheds are common shelters for Virginia opossums. The only marsupial of North America, the opossum is born the size of a bumblebee and nurtured in its mother's pouch along with as many as twelve other young opossums.

Attracting Bats

Once considered repugnant by most people, bats have gained a much better reputation as their role as bug control agents has become recognized. If you wish to lure bats, consider erecting a bat house (below). It will be easier to attract them if they are already living in your area and if there is a pond or a lake close by. Set the house out of reach of predators, at least ten to twenty feet (3 to 6 m) above ground and facing southeast. Try to position it so that there is an unobstructed flight path approaching it that is at least three feet (1 m) in length. Once you have installed the house, be patient; months or even years may pass before bats begin using it.

Perhaps the most intimidating of city squatters are skunks. When spied at a distance, ambling through a neighborhood and followed in single-file by their young, they may seem appealing creatures. And so they are—unless provoked or threatened, when their malodorous scent can be accurately delivered to a target at a distance of up to thirteen feet (4 m).

Reading the Signs

A habitat may resemble a ghost town unless you know where to look and what you are seeing. Learn to read the clues. Tracks *(page 74)*, animal droppings, bits of fur, bones, dropped antlers—even an entire dead animal—will transform a seemingly empty world into one with many stories to tell.

Age the tracks: If they appear fresh and finely detailed, it may mean the mammals that made them are not far away. Look for traces of other species nearby for information about possible interactions and check for scat *(below)*. Scat varies according to what the mammal recently fed on. For instance, large bear scat may be laced with blueberries, and can even smell deliciously like them. Winter droppings from deer families are remarkably clean, composed of compressed bark and smelling of a recently chewed tree.

Mammals are creatures of habit: They tend to follow similar routes again and again. These routes, carefully chosen for safety, often lead to feeding or denning areas. Look in meadows for mouse runways in the grass or snow; these show up like etched patterns as snow melts in warm weather. The long, slightly raised humps in a lawn signal the presence of mole tunnels under the grass. Beaten trails are left by larger mammals, such as beaver, deer, and caribou. Once you become aware of animal trails, a virtual road map is revealed, complete with intersections and homes.

SHELTER

Mammal homes come in many shapes and sizes. Associated signs such as scat, tracks, or fur may help you figure out which mammal is the architect. Deer bed down; the imprints left by their body are particularly evident where snow has been compacted and melted by body heat, but crushed grass beneath a fruit tree may also be an indication of a deer bedding area. A careful search in a field may reveal the grassy nest of a vole or a mouse or the second-hand winter

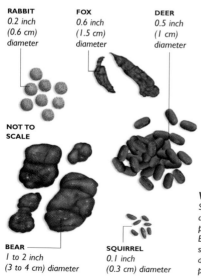

RABBIT
0.2 inch
(0.6 cm)
diameter

FOX
0.6 inch
(1.5 cm)
diameter

DEER
0.5 inch
(1 cm)
diameter

NOT TO SCALE

BEAR
1 to 2 inch
(3 to 4 cm) diameter

SQUIRREL
0.1 inch
(0.3 cm) diameter

Who Dung It?

Scat, also called feces or droppings, supply important clues about mammals, identifying species, diet, and even time of passing. Old scat are likely to be bleached white by the sun. Examine scat for bits of nuts, fruit, and shells, and even smell them for telltale signs; but avoid touching mammal droppings with your hands since they may contain harmful parasites that can be transmitted to humans.

Hair caught on a barbed-wire fence marks the recent passage of a deer.

home of deer mice or white-footed mice: a roofed-over bird's nest.

Many mammal homes are underground—benign zones offering protection from severe weather and predators. Expert diggers include armadillos, prairie dogs, badgers, woodchucks, and, of course, moles. Their dens serve as shelters for other animals as well: Skunks, opossums, squirrels, and snakes are just a few of the free-loading tenants that may move in after a den is abandoned. Foxes, coyotes, and wolves often prefer

to renovate, enlarging an existing den first before taking it over. If you spot a den, never stick your hand inside—even if it looks empty. You may get bitten.

Another sign to keep an eye out for are leftovers. Blood and fur may indicate where a coyote killed and ate a cottontail rabbit. The frayed tips of young trees and branches are usually a sign that deer have been by—lacking top incisors, deer tend to rip the twigs off foliage when they eat. Compare these uneven cuts to the clean, angled ones made by sharp-toothed rabbits and rodents such as woodchucks; they almost look like they were made by pruning shears. Beavers leave just stumps behind as they cut down entire trees for feeding and building dams.

Beavers dig canals, such as the one at left, to help them escape predators and to provide a route for taking logs back to their den.

Tracks & Trails

Here is a selection of tracks grouped into three categories according to the ways mammal feet touch the ground. In each case, the upper track is the front foot, the lower one the hind foot. Herbivores and omnivores such as rodents, lagomorphs, and bears have a plantigrade, or flat-footed, posture, which leaves tracks that show the soles of the feet as well as the toes—and in some cases, claws. Carnivores such as felines and canids have digitigrade posture; their tracks reveal how they run on the balls of their feet, "heels" off the ground. Artiodactyls (even-toed ungulates)

PLANTIGRADE

Red squirrel (Tamiasciurus hudsonicus) Bounding pattern leaves hind prints farther apart and ahead of smaller fore prints.
0.8 INCH (2 CM)
1.5 INCHES (4 CM)

Striped skunk (Mephitis mephitis) Imprint of vestigial thumb near inner heel pad may be visible.
1 TO 2 INCHES (3 TO 5 CM)
1 TO 2 INCHES (3 TO 5 CM)

Raccoon (Procyon lotor) Toe pads continuous with heel pads; see trail pattern, far right.
3 INCHES (7.5 CM)
3 TO 4 INCHES (7.5 TO 11 CM)

Porcupine (Erethizon dorsatum) Palm and heel pads may look spotty.
2.5 INCHES (6 CM)
3 INCHES (7.5 CM)

Beaver (Castor canadensis) Hind feet webbed; good tracks rare because often obliterated by tail drag.
3 INCHES (7.5 CM)
6 INCHES (15 CM)

Black bear (Ursus americanus) When walking, hind foot usually oversteps front foot; claws visible.
4 INCHES (10 CM)
7 TO 9 INCHES (18 TO 23 CM)

DIGITIGRADE

Bobcat (Lynx rufus) Similar to print of large domestic cat.
2 INCHES (5 CM)
2 INCHES (5 CM)

Red fox (Vulpes vulpes) Pad impressions widely spaced.
2 INCHES (5.5 CM)
2 INCHES (5 CM)

Fisher (Martes pennanti) Fifth toe occasionally visible on outside of track.
2 TO 4 INCHES (5 TO 10 CM)
2 TO 3 INCHES (5 TO 7.5 CM)

Coyote (Canis latrans) Claw imprints always in evidence.
2.5 INCHES (6 CM)
2 INCHES (5.5 CM)

Gray wolf (Canis lupus) Inner toes often appear larger than outer toes.
4 TO 5 INCHES (11 TO 13 CM)
3 TO 5 INCHES (7.5 TO 13 CM)

Wolverine (Gulo gulo) Fifth toe occasionally visible on outside of track.
4 TO 8 INCHES (10 TO 20 CM)
3 TO 4 INCHES (7.5 TO 10 CM)

leave split-hoof marks; some, such as deer and caribou, include the imprint of their dewclaws—toes at the back of the legs—when they walk on soft terrain or snow. Perissodactyls (odd-toed ungulates) such as horses and donkeys produce a single, unbroken mark with their unsplit hoof.

A TRIO OF TRAILS

An estimate of the speed and gait of a mammal can be determined by the spacing and placement of tracks. Walking trail patterns of three different mammals appear below.

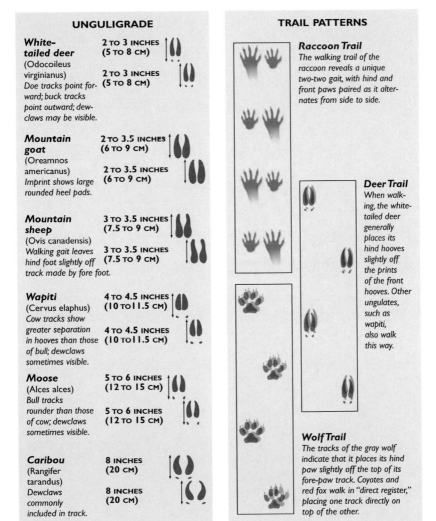

UNGULIGRADE

White-tailed deer
2 TO 3 INCHES (5 TO 8 CM)
2 TO 3 INCHES (5 TO 8 CM)
(Odocoileus virginianus) Doe tracks point forward; buck tracks point outward; dewclaws may be visible.

Mountain goat
2 TO 3.5 INCHES (6 TO 9 CM)
2 TO 3.5 INCHES (6 TO 9 CM)
(Oreamnos americanus) Imprint shows large rounded heel pads.

Mountain sheep
3 TO 3.5 INCHES (7.5 TO 9 CM)
3 TO 3.5 INCHES (7.5 TO 9 CM)
(Ovis canadensis) Walking gait leaves hind foot slightly off track made by fore foot.

Wapiti
4 TO 4.5 INCHES (10 TO 11.5 CM)
4 TO 4.5 INCHES (10 TO 11.5 CM)
(Cervus elaphus) Cow tracks show greater separation in hooves than those of bull; dewclaws sometimes visible.

Moose
5 TO 6 INCHES (12 TO 15 CM)
5 TO 6 INCHES (12 TO 15 CM)
(Alces alces) Bull tracks rounder than those of cow; dewclaws sometimes visible.

Caribou
8 INCHES (20 CM)
8 INCHES (20 CM)
(Rangifer tarandus) Dewclaws commonly included in track.

TRAIL PATTERNS

Raccoon Trail
The walking trail of the raccoon reveals a unique two-two gait, with hind and front paws paired as it alternates from side to side.

Deer Trail
When walking, the white-tailed deer generally places its hind hooves slightly off the prints of the front hooves. Other ungulates, such as wapiti, also walk this way.

Wolf Trail
The tracks of the gray wolf indicate that it places its hind paw slightly off the top of its fore-paw track. Coyotes and red fox walk in "direct register," placing one track directly on top of the other.

Seasonal Guide

In the fall, the wide-ranging North American porcupine (Erethizon dorsatum) feeds on a variety of vegetation, including corn, acorns, and, as this porcupine in Montana is doing, mountain ash berries. In the winter, however, the porcupine tends to feed primarily on tree bark, especially conifers.

Because the life of mammals revolves around circadian and seasonal rhythms, the time of day and year is often an important factor in finding them. For example, during the summer months, many seemingly deserted areas come alive at dusk. In the winter, however, the peak period may shift to noon when it is warmest.

Seasonal rhythms matter less in tropical, subtropical, and warm-desert climates where the weather is generally mild. But in the regions of North America and northern Europe where temperatures drop steeply in winter, mammal behavior may undergo marked shifts. When walking in the woods in late summer and autumn, you'll see and hear signs of mammals' busy preparations. The hibernators—creatures such as ground squirrels, marmots, and chipmunks—are gorging on nuts and berries to add a layer of energy-rich fat to their body. Look for gray squirrels scurrying here and there, burying one nut at a time under leaves—a bank account of food to be withdrawn when needed. Other squirrels, such as red squirrels and chipmunks, hoard nuts and seeds in huge batches. Beavers don't hibernate, but stay active all winter long beneath the ice. They stick tree branches in the mud at the bottom of ponds, a cache of gnawable bark to get them through the cold season.

Some mammals escape winter by migrating. Humpback whales swim from waters in the northern Pacific and Atlantic to warmer seas. In the far north, caribou move from the tundra to areas south of the tree line, while bighorn sheep and mountain goats descend mountains into more protected valleys.

The eastern fox squirrel (Sciurus niger) makes its home in the cavity of a tree, occasionally building additional sleeping quarters of leaves—called drays—when necessary.

RUTTING BEHAVIOR

Male ungulates—wapiti, white-tailed deer, and moose—rut in the fall. In some areas, such as the foothills of the Rockies, the air may resound with the bugling of a bull wapiti as he tries to attract more females to his harem. A fortunate tracker may even come upon two bulls, their antlers locked over the right to mate with a doe. If that happens, watch out. The behavior of ungulates in rut is highly unpredictable.

In autumn, most mammals in cold areas molt their shorter, summer hair, replacing it with a thicker coat of fur. The furry pelt of canids such as wolves keeps their body dry even when covered with snow.

Champion among the pelt-bearers is the sea otter, its all-season coat made of some 800 million tightly packed hairs. Sea otters have to survive in near-freezing waters year-round without a seal's or a whale's thick layer of blubber.

LIFE IN A COLD CLIMATE

Winter is the time of the year when tracking may be easiest since snow—especially a light covering less than an inch (2.5 cm) deep— leaves the clearest prints *(page 74)*. Wapiti and other deer try to save energy by following the same trails through the deep snow again and again, packing it down for easier passage. The snow tends to restrict their movements to a relatively small tramped-down area, called a deer yard.

Thumbing their nose at winter, some mammals pass the cold months in a state of suspended animation.

The semi-aquatic muskrat (Ondatra zibethicus) builds a lodge of cut vegetation in marshes and along the banks of streams.

Tracks of the meadow vole (Microtus pennsylvanicus) *mark the pristine snow in southern Alberta. Voles also tunnel beneath the snow, using it as a security blanket for warmth and shelter.*

Ground squirrels, marmots, and many bats are particularly efficient hibernators. Of them, the woodchuck (also called the groundhog) is the best known, with legendary significance ascribed to its emergence on Groundhog Day. Not long after the first frost, the woodchuck disappears into its burrow where it gradually slows its body processes almost to the point of death. Its heart rate, normally about a hundred beats per minute, drops to fifteen or lower. Its body temperature plummets from 98.6 degrees Fahrenheit (37°C) to about 40 degrees Fahrenheit (4°C). Respiration may slow to one breath every six minutes. During the weeks that follow, the woodchuck may awaken from this living *rigor mortis* once or twice, even walk about in mild weather, before returning to hibernate until spring.

Few mammals pass the winter like the woodchuck. Raccoons and skunks, for instance, merely slow down, conserving their energy by denning and emerging during warmer spells to look for food. And black bears enter a shallow hypothermia, their body functions remaining at a level where the females can still give birth and nurse their young.

Some animals change in appearance to help them survive winter. As a snowshoe hare molts, gray-brown fur becomes mottled with white, finally switching to a pure white winter coat. Arctic hares, foxes, and weasels have also adopted this camouflage technique. But most mammals do not change color, in part because gray and brown coats can provide adequate concealment in shadows and against vegetation even in the snowy winter. Also, a white animal will tend to stand out during a sudden thaw or spring melt, suddenly becoming a tempting meal for a predator.

Hunger is a mammal's constant companion during a cold winter. Food is almost always difficult to find and usually less nutritious. Deer, for example, try to survive by eating tree twigs and bark, sometimes getting so little nutrition from the diet that they may starve to death on a full stomach.

SLOW RECOVERY

Spring brings release from winter's bondage. Hibernators emerge, migrators return, and white animals revert to brown. This is the time for most of winter's survivors to give birth and raise their young. The female ungulates that inspired a racket in the fall are now giving birth, as are the rodents and lagomorphs, some of which will continue to produce litters throughout the summer.

Spring is also feast after famine. Hibernators have an emaciated appearance. It will take all summer and into the fall for them to regain the poundage they lost during their winter sleep. Deer and moose can sometimes be spotted licking vegetation left salty by road maintenance crews, and porcupines and woodchucks may be seen, their nose to the ground, as they lick salty stones by the side of a road.

As spring turns to summer, many mammals are kept busy raising their young. This is the best time to see family groups traveling or playing together. Early morning walkers may be rewarded with a glimpse of a doe and her fawn feeding at the forest's edge or, if extremely lucky, with the sight of a pair of fox cubs playing outside their den.

In Alaska's Denali National Park, well-trodden tracks in the tundra (left) mark the route taken by caribou (Rangifer tarandus) when they travel to their calving grounds in the spring.

After a long winter, a young grizzly bear (Ursus arctos) in Yellowstone National Park hungrily gnaws on a tree, probably in search of grubs to eat.

Back from the Brink

F ossil records suggest a historical rate of mammal extinction of one species every two hundred years. From 1600 to 1996, though, records show that eighty-six mammal species have been lost. The World Monitoring Centre currently lists 681 mammal species as endangered *(page 181)*. These figures evoke what some scientists fear will be an "extinction event" comparable to the demise of the dinosaur sixty-six million years ago. Noted zoologist E. O. Wilson, for one, believes that without a change in trends, nearly half of all the species of plants and animals on the planet will disappear by the end of the next century.

In the recent past, overexploitation was blamed for the decimation of many animal species—notably the American bison, the beaver, and many marine

Plans to extract salt from Baja's Laguna San Ignacio threaten the gray whale (Eschrichtius robustus). Every winter gray whales travel five thousand miles (8,000 km)—one of the animal kingdom's longest migrations—to give birth to their young in the shallow waters there.

mammals. Hunting—especially poaching—is still a real danger, but the number one threat to species survival is now perceived to be habitat destruction. Population pressures in Africa, India, Asia, and South America, in particular, have meant the loss of natural habitats to farmland and expanding settlements. Added to the direct destruction have been the accompanying debilitating effects of changes in rainfall, watersheds, weather, and air quality. Wildlife protection agencies such as the World Wildlife Fund are responding by broadening their focus from protection of individual species to preservation of the habits they inhabit.

The sea otter (*Enhydra lutris*) is a case in point. Reduced by the fur trade to a population of only about thirty animals, sea otters began a successful comeback following a 1911 international treaty. But the numbers are once again dropping. One reason for their decline off Alaska may be that they have become a mainstay in the diet of local killer whales (*Orcinus orca*). Depletion of fish stocks in the region has precipitated the collapse of pinniped populations, including Steller sea lions (*Eumetopias jubatus*) and harbor seals (*Phoca vitulina*), traditional prey of killer whales.

Perhaps the most renowned endangered species is the giant panda (*Ailuropoda melanoleuca*). Because the bamboo forests of southwestern China periodically die off, giant pandas are forced to migrate to other forests in search of bamboo, their diet staple—a natural cycle that ensures genetic diversity of the species. Today's isolated pockets of bamboo forests, however, prevent such migration, which has been devastating for the species. One remedy currently under discussion is the creation of wilderness corridors between zones of bamboo forest to encourage migration of giant pandas.

Restricted habitat and specialized mating behavior threaten the Indiana bat (*Myotis sodalis*). Human activities have disrupted large hibernating populations that congregate in caves and abandoned mines in the eastern United States, causing a dramatic drop in numbers—from an estimated 120,000 in 1975 to 20,000 in 1995. Delayed fertilization *(page 41)* results in a massive birthing of Indiana bats in the spring, but only if populations survive hibernation.

Human technology, ironically, may hold a last hope for some species. The lowland gorilla of central Africa faces the triple threat of habitat loss, poaching, and war. Consolidated international efforts have improved the success rate in captive breeding of this species and reproductive technologies—including in vitro fertilization—are playing a role in maintaining a healthy, genetically diverse group. However, as long as its home continues to be under siege, reintroduction programs are effectively stymied.

Destruction of hardwood forests in the coastal region of southeastern Brazil has imperiled the golden lion tamarin (Leontopithecus rosalia). Fewer than six hundred remain in the wild.

MAMMALS:
AN INTERNATIONAL BIOME GUIDE

The world's biomes are zones of biogeography based on vegetation and shaped by the region's temperature range and precipitation.

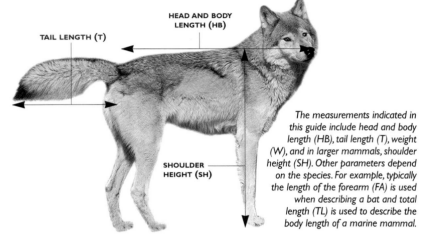

HEAD AND BODY LENGTH (HB)

TAIL LENGTH (T)

SHOULDER HEIGHT (SH)

The measurements indicated in this guide include head and body length (HB), tail length (T), weight (W), and in larger mammals, shoulder height (SH). Other parameters depend on the species. For example, typically the length of the forearm (FA) is used when describing a bat and total length (TL) is used to describe the body length of a marine mammal.

This guide contains the profiles of more than 150 mammals, grouped according to nine biomes, or zones of life, worldwide *(map, pages 84 to 85)*. As one moves away from the equator, the diversity of life—biodiversity—generally diminishes. An area of tropical forest near Panama City, for instance,

may be home to more than 140 species of mammals, whereas an area of comparative size in the prairie land of eastern Kansas may hold about 55 species and a similarly sized area of the Alaskan tundra may contain only 16 species.

Opportunities for greater biodiversity are created within so-called

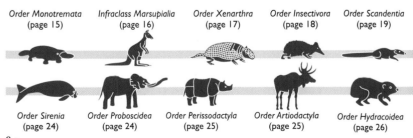

Order Monotremata (page 15)

Infraclass Marsupialia (page 16)

Order Xenarthra (page 17)

Order Insectivora (page 18)

Order Scandentia (page 19)

Order Sirenia (page 24)

Order Proboscidea (page 24)

Order Perissodactyla (page 25)

Order Artiodactyla (page 25)

Order Hydracoidea (page 26)

———————————

ECHIDNA / *Tachyglossus aculeatus*

ICON OF ORDER OR INFRACLASS
For the full list, see opposite and below.

The echidna, or spiny anteater, is one of two species in the genus *Tachyglossus* that—along with the duck-billed platypus *(page 97)*—make up the egg-laying monotremes *(page 15)*. It has a toothless mouth with a long sticky tongue for lapping up ants and termites. Mixed in with the hair on its back are hard quills; its stomach is covered in fur. The quills appear about fifty-five days after hatching, at which point the infant is no longer carried in the pouch but left in a sheltered place. For the next three months, the mother returns regularly to nurse it, but instead of nipples, she has—like the platypus—specialized areas of skin that exude milk. When threatened, this nocturnal creature burrows into the ground or rolls up into a spiny ball.

BRIEF DESCRIPTION

FAMILY
Tachyglossidae
RANGE
Australia, New Guinea, Tasmania
HABITAT
Arid regions, including grasslands, forests, and rocky areas
SIZE
HB 12 to 18 inches (30 to 45 cm); T 3 to 3.5 inches (7 to 9 cm); W 5.5 to 13 pounds (2.5 to 6 kg)
LIFE CYCLE
Mating July to August; usually one egg laid, incubated 9 to 27 days; hatched young stays in pouch until quills grow

KEY FACTS

ecotones, zones of gradation between biomes. For example, the edges of the California chaparral support many types of aridland rodents, which in turn attract a variety of predators from the bordering forested region.

When using the guide *(pages 86 to 174)*, note that each mammal profile is accompanied by an icon showing the mammal's order or in the case of marsupials, infraclass *(opposite and below)*. For more information on the classification of mammals, refer to page 14.

As you read each profile, keep in mind that a species may live in more than one biome; its selection for a particular one in this guide implies that the species is a characteristic resident of the biome. The ability of a species to live in more than one biome is a tribute to its ability to adapt. Bats are especially adaptable; they are found in every biome, except the tundra, altering form and behavior to suit a variety of food sources. Rodents, lagomorphs, carnivores, and ungulates all have desert and tundra representatives, each with remarkable adaptations for survival. Their stories are discussed further in the introduction to each biome section.

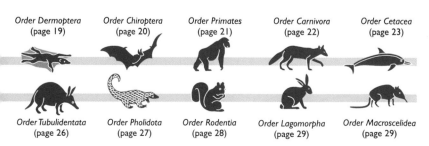

Order Dermoptera
(page 19)

Order Chiroptera
(page 20)

Order Primates
(page 21)

Order Carnivora
(page 22)

Order Cetacea
(page 23)

Order Tubulidentata
(page 26)

Order Pholidota
(page 27)

Order Rodentia
(page 28)

Order Lagomorpha
(page 29)

Order Macroscelidea
(page 29)

Map of World Biomes

 Alpine
(page 86)
The climate of this high-altitude biome varies according to the elevation.
Location determines the altitudes at
which the tundra conditions occur.

 Tropical forest
(page 96)
Equatorial rain forests (such as those in Central and
South America, central West Africa, and Southeast Asia)
and tropical seasonal semi-evergreen forests (such as
those of northern Australia, the Caribbean, and India)
both receive considerable amounts of rainfall. Only the
seasonal forests, however, also experience significant
dry seasons.
Mean annual rainfall: 24 to 93 inches (61 to 237 cm)
Mean annual temperature: 77°F (25°C)

Temperate grassland
(page 142)
Warm, even temperatures
coupled with low rainfall favor
the dominance of grasses over
trees and shrubs in these large,
predominantly flat areas.
Mean annual rainfall: 10 to
30 inches (25 to 75cm)
Mean annual temperature:
50°F (10°C)

Temperate forest
(page 150)
Even rainfall and a long growing season
characterize this temperate biome, which
supports deciduous and mixed forests.
Mean annual rainfall: 29 inches (74 cm)
Mean annual temperature: 48°F (9°C)

Northern coniferous forest
(page 160)
Drier than temperate forest, the taiga,
or boreal forest, is known for a short, cool
growing season and long, harsh winter.
Mean annual rainfall: 18 inches (47 cm)
Mean annual temperature: 33°F (0.5°C)

 **Tropical grassland & savanna**
(page 118)

In spite of a wide range of rainfall accumulation, soil types and drainage play a major role in supporting similar types of vegetation throughout the various regions of this biome.
Mean annual rainfall: 29 to 68 inches (74 to 172 cm)
Mean annual temperature: 66°F (19°C)

 Aridland
(page 128)

This biome is made up of desert, chaparral, and tropical scrub forest. Low levels of rainfall, uninterrupted winds, drainage, and soil quality all contribute to this biome's sparse vegetation.
Mean annual rainfall: 2 to 9 inches (4 to 23 cm)
Mean annual temperature: 64°F (18°C)

 Tundra
(page 166)

Short winter days and strong uninterrupted winds characterize this biome's severe climate.
Mean annual rainfall: 7 inches (17 cm)
Mean annual temperature: 19°F (-7°C)

 Marine
(page 170)

The great heat capacity of the oceans ensures relative uniformity in temperature, except near land. Surface waters, however, are often divided biogeographically by high, middle, and tropical latitudes.

Alpine

Climbing a mountain is like traveling northward: For each 650-foot (200-m) -rise in elevation, the average temperature drops about two degrees Fahrenheit (1°C). This is because the atmosphere becomes thinner the farther away it is from Earth's surface and thinner air is able to hold less heat. As well, cold air holds less moisture than warm air, so as air rises and cools, it gets drier, causing biomes to gradually change with elevation, in some cases paralleling the shift in biomes—from rain forest to temperate deciduous forest to coniferous forest to tundra—that occurs as one travels from the equator to the north pole.

Another factor that contributes to the change in climate is the effect of mountains on trade winds. When trade winds carrying clouds are forced upward by mountains, they release rainfall at higher levels. In the tropics and subtropics, when the mountains intercept warm, moist air from the sea, a "cloud forest," or montane rain forest, may be created, typically at sixty-five hundred to ten thousand feet (2,000 to 3,000 m). Unlike the vegetation of a tropical rain forest, which is characterized by a tall canopy, the vegetation of a cloud forest is dominated by short, crooked trees, mosses, masses of epiphytes, and a rich ferny understory.

Above this moist belt of vegetation lies the alpine tun-

dra. The point where this line begins varies greatly according to the climate of the region. For instance, on certain mountains in Scandinavia, the tundra line occurs at altitudes of two thousand feet (600 m), while on mountains in Venezuela near the equator, the tundra line occurs at about thirteen thousand feet (4,000 m). At these heights, strong, uninterrupted winds create chill factors of devastating proportions. The miniature juniper forests of the Colorado Rockies are good examples of trees on the "front lines" of the alpine tundra. Twisted and bent by wind and ice, the junipers actually shift position, loosening and regaining their grip on rock.

The mammals that inhabit the higher altitudes deal with cold in a variety of ways. The larger ones, such as the mountain sheep (*Ovis canadensis*) and its predator the mountain lion (*Felis concolor*), descend to warmer pastures in the autumn, while many smaller mammals hibernate *(page 11)* or take shelter. For instance, the meadow vole (*Microtus pennsylvanicus*) is active year-round, inhabiting a labyrinth of burrows under the snow. For these mammals, survival in low temperatures means maintaining a very high metabolic rate.

Large size is a more economical way to combat the cold. A greater overall mass in relation to surface area means valuable heat is more effectively retained. Size combined with thick fur insulation enables alpine species such as the mountain goat (*Oreamnos americanus*) to inhabit regions above the tree line year-round. Specialized hooves aid such mountain ungulates in coping with rocky terrain and steep cliffs. Those of the mountain goat are almost pincerlike. They open and close, serving as brakes during a descent or as a grip on a rocky ridge. A textured, cushioned foot pad provides the hoof with secure, suction-cuplike traction.

Finally, as any climber knows, the rarified oxygen content of thin mountain air poses breathing challenges. In response to this, the Andean vicuña (*Vicugna vicugna*) has developed a form of hemoglobin with an enhanced affinity for oxygen. This trait, coupled with its remarkably thick fur, makes the vicuña one of the highest-living mammals, inhabiting lofty alpine summits more than sixteen thousand feet (5,000 m) up.

This idealized mountain slope reflects the changing life zones that occur with elevation. At the lower elevations, conditions don't differ much from the surrounding lowlands. However, as the temperature decreases with height, open grasslands and mixed deciduous woodlands give way first to coniferous forests and then alpine meadows, where trees are stunted and wild flowers flourish. Farther up, these begin to die out until gradually only a few hardy lichens cling to the rock and gravel. At the very top lies a zone of permanent ice and snow.

SHREW OPOSSUM / *Caenolestes fuliginosus*

This marsupial gets its common name from the shrewlike appearance created by its elongated head, small eyes, and rounded ears. Unlike most marsupials, the shrew opossum has no pouch in which to hold the young. It is predominantly nocturnal and is usually found scurrying through leaf litter along runways. Capable of climbing trees, it prefers moist areas with thick vegetation that provides cover and hiding places from predators. Little is known about its diet, but the shrew opossum is believed to be chiefly insectivorous. It has also been known to scavenge meat and kill small newborn rodents.

FAMILY
Caenolestidae
RANGE
Northwestern South America
HABITAT
Alpine forests and meadows
SIZE
HB 3.5 to 5 inches (9 to 13.5 cm); T 3 to 5 inches (8 to 13 cm); W 0.7 to 1.4 ounces (20 to 40 g)
LIFE CYCLE
Little is known; mating probably in July, at least three or four young born

PYRENEAN DESMAN / *Galemys pyrenaicus*

The molelike desman has a long snout that makes it look more like a shrew than a mole. It has webbed feet, a rudderlike tail, and short thick fur, adaptations to its semi-aquatic lifestyle. The desman does not have a thick insulating layer of blubber; instead, its pelage is kept waterproof by oily skin secretions. It grooms air into its coat, which not only prevents heat loss, but also helps the animal rise to the surface quickly after diving in search of crustaceans. Insect larvae are another dietary staple, and the desman uses its sensory vibrissae to locate food and possibly also to orient itself in its environment—its eyes are greatly reduced and can only see changes in light. During the day, it sleeps rolled up in a ball in narrow burrows along river banks. Habitat changes and water pollution threaten this unique creature with extinction.

FAMILY
Talpidae
RANGE
Iberia (France, Spain, and Portugal)
HABITAT
Rapid-flowing montane streams
SIZE
HB 4 to 5 inches (10 to 13 cm); T 5 to 6 inches (13 to 15.5 cm); W 1.4 to 2.8 ounces (40 to 80 g)
LIFE CYCLE
Mating probably January to May; gestation about 30 days, one to five young born; usually two litters per year

SNOW LEOPARD / *Uncia uncia*

With less than five thousand snow leopards left, the chances of seeing this creature in the wild are slim. To make the odds even worse, this creature is crepuscular and nocturnal. It wanders over a large home range in search of prey, including yaks *(page 90)*, mountain goats *(page 90)*, and bharals *(page 92)*. Like many big cats, it leads a solitary life, only coming together with members of the opposite sex to mate. Despite its protected status, this species is still hunted and its skins are sold on the black market. In addition, it has lost some of its habitat to agriculture, which has also threatened its favored prey. Hunting livestock almost inevitably results in its death at the hands of farmers.

FAMILY
Felidae
RANGE
Central Asia
HABITAT
Alpine meadows and rocky areas at 4,800 to 16,000 feet (1,500 to 4,900 m)
SIZE
HB 30 to 56 inches (75 to 142 cm); T 31.5 to 39 inches (80 to 100 cm); SH 20 to 26 inches (50 to 65 cm); W 55 to 165 pounds (25 to 75 kg)
LIFE CYCLE
Mating January to March; gestation 98 to 103 days, usually two or three cubs born

ANDEAN CAT / *Oreailurus jacobita*

The Andean cat is extremely rare, has never been kept in captivity, and has seldom been observed alive in the wild. Thus, the little information that is known about the species comes from museum specimens, odd sightings, and hunters and their trophies. Slightly larger than a house cat, the species lives at elevations above ten thousand feet (3,000 m) in semi-arid, windy, cold, and treeless regions. It eats birds and small mammals, principally various species of the chinchilla family. The inaccessible nature of its habitat may prevent human development from threatening the future of this cat. However, some research suggests that air pollution is harming the native vegetation in the area, which in turn may affect many of the prey species of this rare and beautiful alpine mammal.

FAMILY
Felidae
RANGE
Andes of southern Peru, Bolivia, Chile, and Argentina
HABITAT
Rocky, often snow-covered areas at high elevations
SIZE
HB 24 inches (60 cm); T 14 inches (35 cm); W 8 to 15 pounds (3.5 to 7 kg)
LIFE CYCLE
Nothing is known about reproductive biology

YAK / *Bos grunniens*

There may be less than a couple of thousand wild yaks left in the wild. They travel great distances seeking lichens, mosses, grasses, and herbs to eat. Their large hooves help them to walk in snow and dig for food. Well-adapted to cold climate, they fare poorly in warmer places. Excessive hunting for its meat and coat have imperiled the species. Millions of much smaller domesticated yaks are commonly used for heavy labor, such as pulling carts; for milk and meat; and as a source of wool, which is processed from their pelage.

FAMILY
Bovidae
RANGE
Tibet
HABITAT
Plateaus at 13,500 to 20,000 feet (4,100 to 6,100 m)

SIZE
HB 8 to 11 feet (2.5 to 3.3 m); T 20 to 31.5 inches (51 to 80 cm); SH 5.6 to 6.6 feet (1.7 to 2 m); W 1,600 to 2,200 pounds (730 to 1,000 kg)
LIFE CYCLE
Mating September to October; gestation 250 to 260 days, one calf born

MOUNTAIN GOAT / *Oreamnos americanus*

The mountain goat isn't a true goat; it is more like a mountain antelope, but it has many features in common with goats and so it is placed in its own genus. Mountain goats are considered the best rock climbers in North America and readily move along small ledges, up steep slopes, and across deep chasms. Their impressive climbing skills permit them to forage in small alpine meadows that are inaccessible to other animals; there they feed on grasses, sedges, lichens, and occasionally the leaves and shoots of shrubs. Both sexes possess curved black horns, which are used to help age individuals. At about two years of age, a ring is formed in each horn, and every subsequent year a new ring is added; by counting rings, age can be calculated.

FAMILY
Bovidae
RANGE
Western Canada, United States
HABITAT
Alpine rocky regions and meadows
SIZE
HB 3.6 to 6.2 feet (1.1 to 1.9 m); T 3.5 to 7.5 inches (9 to 19 cm); SH 35 to 39 inches (90 to 100 cm); W 100 to 249 pounds (45.5 to 113 kg)
LIFE CYCLE
Mating October to December; gestation 147 to 178 days, one or two kids born

CHAMOIS / *Rupicapra rupicapra*

Distinctive hook-shaped horns distinguish chamois. Remarkably agile, it can gallop on uneven, rocky ground and jump up to six feet (2 m) high. Its nimbleness and acrobatics give it access to hard-to-reach areas, easing competition for the grasses, herbs, and flowers it prefers to eat. In winter when food is scarce, it dines on pine shoots, lichens, and mosses. Males live a solitary life; they are territorial and fight for a harem at mating time. Females and young usually form herds of five to thirty members. A posted sentinel warns the others of danger by stamping its feet and emitting a high-pitched whistle through its nose.

FAMILY
Bovidae
RANGE
Europe and western Asia
HABITAT
Alpine rocky areas and meadows at 3,300 to 11,500 feet (1,000 to 3,500 m)
SIZE
HB 35 to 51 inches (90 to 130 cm); T 4 to 6 inches (10 to 15 cm); SH 28 to 31.5 inches (70 to 80 cm);

W 48 to 136 pounds (22 to 62 kg)
LIFE CYCLE
Mating October to November; gestation 170 to 180 days, one (rarely two or three) kids born

IBEX / *Capra ibex*

Males have much larger horns than females, up to fifty-five inches (140 cm) and fifteen inches (38 cm) respectively.

Females and young form herds of ten to twenty; males form separate herds, but sighting of solitary males is common. At mating time, males aggressively rear on hindlegs and smash horns to fight for females. Ibex have been hunted as trophies and for meat and medicinal purposes; they now face habitat loss to agriculture and resource competition with domestic goats.

FAMILY
Bovidae
RANGE
Central Europe; southwest Asia; northeastern Sudan and northern Ethiopia
HABITAT
Alpine rocky cliffs, meadows, and arid highlands at tree line to 22,000 feet (6,700 m)
SIZE
HB 3.9 to 5.8 feet (1.2 to 1.7 m); T 4 to 8 inches (10 to 20 cm); SH 25.6 to 41.3 inches (65 to 105 cm); W 77 to 330 pounds (35 to 150 kg)
LIFE CYCLE
Mating December to January; gestation 150 to 180 days, one to three young born

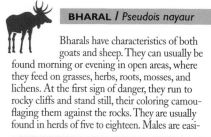

BHARAL / *Pseudois nayaur*

Bharals have characteristics of both goats and sheep. They can usually be found morning or evening in open areas, where they feed on grasses, herbs, roots, mosses, and lichens. At the first sign of danger, they run to rocky cliffs and stand still, their coloring camouflaging them against the rocks. They are usually found in herds of five to eighteen. Males are easily distinguished from females because they are larger and have horns up to thirty inches (80 cm) long; those of females rarely exceed eight inches (20 cm). Males possess strong necks and skulls up to two inches (5 cm) thick—requirements to withstand the horn-crashing with another male during mating season.

FAMILY
Bovidae
RANGE
South central Asia (Himalayas)
HABITAT
Alpine cliffs and meadows at 10,000 to 17,600 feet (3,000 to 5,400 m)
SIZE
HB 3.6 to 5.6 feet (1.1 to 1.7 m);
T 4 to 8 inches (10 to 20 cm);
SH 28 to 90 inches (70 to 90 cm);
W 77 to 169 pounds (35 to 75 kg)
LIFE CYCLE
Mating October to November; gestation 150 to 165 days, one lamb (rarely two) born

DALL SHEEP / *Ovis dalli*

Named after U.S. zoologist W.H. Dall, this agile creature is also called the white sheep. It is usually found in groups of five to ten, feeding on grasses, sedges, and herbs growing on steep rocky terrain where access is difficult for others—including predators. Winter movement to lower areas offers better feeding grounds, and large migratory groups often form as a safety-in-numbers measure on the open, flat ground, where they are vulnerable. The sexes stay segregated during summer and come together during the autumn breeding season, when male aggression runs strong and fierce duels involving violent horn-blows sometimes leave the males stunned. The winners of such contests gain a higher standing in the herd and access to the females.

FAMILY
Bovidae
RANGE
Alaska, northwest Canada
HABITAT
Alpine regions with harsh environments
SIZE
HB 5 to 6 feet (1.4 to 1.8 m); T about 4 inches (10 cm); SH 36 to 40 inches (91 to 102 cm); W 132 to 198 pounds (60 to 90 kg)
LIFE CYCLE
Mating November to December; gestation about 180 days, one lamb born

HOARY MARMOT / *Marmota caligata*

Largest of the North American sciurids, hoary marmots are usually found living in small groups of one male, several females, and their offspring. Their common name refers to their pelage, which is often silvery-gray in color. Early settlers called them whistlers because they let out a shrill whistle to warn others of a threat. When not lying in the sun on lookout rocks, they are usual-ly feeding on vegetation, eating the leaves, the flowers, and the seeds or berries. They hibernate through the winter from October to May (longer or shorter depending on location), drawing on their accumulated fat deposits. Their dens are usually found under large boulders, which prevent large predators such as bears from digging them up.

FAMILY
Sciuridae
RANGE
Northwestern United States through western Canada and into Alaska
HABITAT
Alpine and subalpine slopes
SIZE
HB 18 to 22 inches (45 to 57 cm);
T 5 to 9 inches (13 to 22 cm);
W 7 to 18 pounds (3 to 8 kg)
LIFE CYCLE
Mating April to May; gestation 25 to 30 days, two to five young born

ALPINE MARMOT / *Marmota marmota*

Alpine marmots have distinctive calls. One long whistle warns of an aerial threat such as an eagle, while a series of whistles may warn of an approaching fox. Like other marmots, they are social creatures found in groups of ten to fifteen. They are herbivorous and hibernate in underground chambers, taking advantage of each other's body heat to make it through the winter.

The chambers, although warmer than the ground surface, are cool, moist environments. It was once believed that alpine marmot fat rubbed into the skin could relieve arthritis. The fat was also used as a source of food by mountain peoples and some considered it a delicacy. The spread of agriculture has resulted in this marmot's decline.

FAMILY
Sciuridae
RANGE
European Alps
HABITAT
Open montane areas at 4,700 to 9,000 feet (1,433 to 2,743 m)
SIZE
HB 20 to 24 inches (50 to 60 cm); T 5 to 6 inches (13 to 16 cm); W 5 to 13 pounds (2.5 to 6 kg)
LIFE CYCLE
Gestation 35 to 42 days, two to six young born

AFRICAN MOLE-RAT / *Tachyoryctes splendens*

African mole-rats have small eyes and ears, typical adaptations to subterranean existence. Rather than dig burrows with only the front feet like most other burrowing animals, they use their incisors to scrape soil, then their front and back feet to push it away. Consequently, they prefer areas with loose soil, where complex tunnel systems are easier to build. The tunnels lead to dens and underground food material, especially tubers. Their food preferences make them an agricultural pest in some regions, especially where sweet potatoes and other root crops are grown. Native peoples have often eaten mole-rats in turn, pouring water into their holes, then capturing them as they surface; some peoples believe the pelts are valuable charms.

FAMILY
Muridae
RANGE
Montane areas of eastern Africa
HABITAT
Meadows and open areas at 10,000 to 13,500 feet (3,000 to 4,100 m)

SIZE
HB 6 to 10 inches (16 to 26 cm); T 2 to 4 inches (5 to 9.5 cm); W 7 to 11 ounces (200 to 300 g)
LIFE CYCLE
Mating throughout year, peak at rainy season; gestation 43 to 49 days, one or two young born; often two litters per year

BUSHY-TAILED WOODRAT / *Neotoma cinerea*

Also called packrat, this creature has a habit of stealing shiny objects to add to its den of sticks, bones, and vegetation. A smaller nest is tucked inside the seven- or nine-foot (2- or 3-m) -diameter den, which may be found on cliffs, rock slides, rocky outcroppings, and in caves and canyons. Bushy-tailed woodrats eat mainly green plant matter, but also twigs, nuts, and seeds, some of which may be stored in the pro-

tective outer layer of the nest for later consumption. Although this creature is basically terrestrial, it does climb, making use of its tail for balance, and occasionally it builds its nest in trees at heights of up to fifty feet (15 m). Spotted owls, bobcats, and weasels are just a few of this species' predators. When alarmed, the woodrat makes a loud drumming sound by beating its hind foot against the ground.

FAMILY
Muridae
RANGE
Western United States and Canada
HABITAT
Rocky areas in arctic alpine and arid regions
SIZE
HB 7 to 9 inches (17 to 24 cm);
T 5 to 9 inches (12 to 24 cm);
W 7 to 21 ounces (200 to 600 g)
LIFE CYCLE
Gestation about 35 days, two to six young born in spring or summer

SHORT-TAILED CHINCHILLA / *Chinchilla laniger*

The soft and silky chinchilla is a nocturnal animal that stands upright when eating, looking around as it uses its forearms to lift tubers, roots, mosses, and bulbs to its mouth. A single colony may contain up to a hundred individuals. They shelter in rocky crevices and burrows throughout the foothills and higher elevations of the Chilean Andes. Now bred in captivity on ranches worldwide, this species is almost extinct in the wild due to agricultural expansion, habitat degradation caused by overgrazing by goats, and overhunting for its highly valued fur. It is protected by law, but since the fur of the wild ones is more luxuriant than that of captive-reared individuals, poaching still continues.

FAMILY
Chinchillidae
RANGE
Southern Andes in Chile
HABITAT
Alpine rocky areas and semi-deserts at 2,600 to 5,600 feet (800 to 1,700 m)
SIZE
HB 9 to 15 inches (22 to 38 cm); T 3 to 6 inches (7.5 to 15 cm); W 1 to 2 pounds (0.5 to 0.8 kg)
LIFE CYCLE
Mating May to October; gestation 105 to 115 days, one to six young born; usually two litters per year

AMERICAN PIKA / *Ochotona princeps*

Pikas are diurnal herbivores that stay active throughout the year, including the winter when they survive on stashes of dried vegetation. Summer and autumn they spend most of their time gathering grasses, sedges, and flowering plants, which they leave in piles to dry and then store for the colder months. They live in large colonies, which have individual territories that are defended for nest sites and stored food. Rocky areas with loose soil are used for shelters and nest sites. When pikas eat, their food passes quickly through their digestive system and is only partially digested. Subsequently, certain of their nutrient-rich feces are reingested for further digestion.

FAMILY
Ochotonidae
RANGE
Northwestern United States, western Canada
HABITAT
Rocky terrain in montane regions
SIZE
HB 7 to 8 inches (18 to 21 cm); T not visible; W 3.5 to 7 ounces (100 to 200 g)

LIFE CYCLE
Mating April to July; gestation 30 days, two to five young born; may breed twice yearly depending on locale

Tropical Forest

A typical four-square-mile (10-sq-km) patch of rain forest, such as Pu Mat Forest Reserve, Vietnam (right), is home to more than 1,500 known species of flowering herbs, 750 of trees, 150 of butterflies, 60 of amphibians, 100 of reptiles, 400 of birds, and 125 of mammals. Unfortunately many of these species are endangered today because their habitats are being destroyed to make way for agricultural development.

Tropical forests *(map, pages 84 to 85)* include both evergreen rain forests, such as the ancient forests of the Amazon basin, and seasonal deciduous forests, such as the dry eucalyptus forests of western Australia and Tasmania. Although many species are found in tropical deciduous forests, the greatest diversity of life exists in the true rain forest.

Different mammals thrive at different vertical levels in a tropical forest. Those of the canopy include insectivorous and fruit-eating bats *(page 104)*, as well as primates, squirrels, and other climbing rodents *(page 116)*. Their predators are likely to be snakes and raptors such as hawks and eagles.

Especially adapted to life in the trees are the monkeys, all of which can grasp and hold branches while in rapid motion. New World monkeys such as the spider monkey have the additional help of a prehensile tail—a tail that is also possessed by two rain-forest carnivores, the binturong *(page 110)* and the kinkajou *(page 111)*.

At ground level, anteaters *(page 100)*, peccaries, capybaras, and the semi-aquatic tapir *(page 113)* forage in the rich undergrowth, keeping an eye out for their felid predators—jaguars *(page 111)*, clouded leopards, tigers, and ocelots.

Rarest of the Rare
In the 1990s several new mammals were found in Vietnam's rain forests, including the saola (Pseudoryx nghetinhensis), a goatlike antelope with long curved horns; the manglon (Megamuntiacus vuquangensis), a robust muntjak deer the size of a dog; and a still unnamed rabbit with gray field coat, black stripes, and a reddish patch on its rump (left). Photographed in 1999 by an automatic camera trap set up in the Annamite forest, the red-rumped rabbit is similar to the rare Sumatran rabbit, from which it has been genetically isolated for eight million years.

DUCK-BILLED PLATYPUS / *Ornithorhynchus anatinus*

Equipped with a flat tail and webbed feet, the duck-billed platypus can swim for extended periods underwater searching for food. It uses its leathery bill to probe the soft stream bottom for small invertebrates, vertebrates, and plant material. The platypus stores the food it finds in its cheek pouches and moves up to the surface of the water to eat. The female platypus lays her eggs in burrows in river banks. She lacks nipples and excretes milk from slits in her abdomen instead. When the eggs hatch, the young lap the mother's milk off her abdominal hairs. The male platypus has poisonous glands embedded in his thighs. The glands are connected to spurs on his ankles *(page 34)*. When he fights with another platypus or a predator, he can puncture his opponent with a spur, injecting the animal with poison. In humans the poison produces local pain and sometimes paralysis of an entire limb.

FAMILY
Ornithorhynchidae
RANGE
Eastern Australia, Tasmania
HABITAT
Streams, lakes, and other freshwater systems
SIZE
HB 12 to 18 inches (30 to 45 cm); T 4 to 6 inches (10 to 15 cm); W 1 to 4 pounds (0.5 to 2 kg)
LIFE CYCLE
Usually two eggs laid August to October; incubation 12 to 14 days

SPOTTED CUSCUS / *Phalangista maculata*

When the cuscus was discovered, it was thought to be a monkey because of its prosimian-like movements; it grips branches with its partially hairless, prehensile tail as it travels slowly and deliberately through the rain-forest canopy. It eats leaves, fruit, reptiles, and birds. During the day it rests, usually in a hollowed out part of a tree or on a platform it has made for itself in the branches. Although the male is always spotted, the female usually is not. The largest of the possums, the cuscus is still actively hunted by the people of New Guinea, who value its protein-rich meat.

FAMILY
Phalangeridae
RANGE
New Guinea, surrounding islands of northeastern Australia
HABITAT
Tropical rain forest and mangroves
SIZE
HB 13 to 26 inches (34 to 65 cm); T 12 to 24 inches (31 to 60 cm); W 3 to 13 pounds (1.5 to 6 kg)
LIFE CYCLE
Mating year-round; gestation 13 days, two to four young born; only one survives, staying in mother's pouch for six to seven months

TASMANIAN DEVIL / *Sarcophilus harrisii*

The Tasmanian devil went through a serious decline due to a widespread infectious disease, but its numbers are now recovering—enough for it to be considered a pest by farmers because it preys on sheep and chickens. Many researchers consider this mammal to be the marsupial equivalent of the hyena because of its body shape, short wide snout, and extremely strong jaws, which are capable of crushing bones. Like the hyena, the Tasmanian devil is often described as intelligent and strong. In addition, it runs like a hyena and often feeds on carrion—usually small mammals and fish. It also feeds on live invertebrates, such as beetle larvae. A solitary nocturnal species, it spends the day resting in burrows or grassy nests, which it makes in hollow logs or thick brush. At night it carefully sniffs out prey and waits patiently in ambush.

FAMILY
Dasyuridae
RANGE
Eastern Tasmania; extinct in Australia

HABITAT
Dry eucalyptus forest
SIZE
HB 21 to 30 inches (53 to 76 cm); T 9 to 12 inches (23 to 30 cm); W 9 to 20 pounds (4 to 9 kg)
LIFE CYCLE
Mating March to May; gestation about 31 days, one to four young born

GOODFELLOW'S TREE KANGAROO / *Dendrolagus goodfellowi*

Goodfellow's tree kangaroo, like other tree kangaroos, differs markedly from the terrestrial kangaroo because it has developed various arboreal adaptations, including shorter legs with broad,

cushionlike soles, stocky, strong arms, and a long tail for balance. It can climb smooth tree trunks up to fifteen feet (4.5 m) high and leap long distances. Rare, solitary, and nocturnal, this tree kangaroo may occasionally be seen in the early evening. When it moves on the ground, it takes small hopping steps, alternating between its forearms and hindlegs and holding its tail above the ground in an arched position. In this way, it can reach modest speeds of five miles (8 km) per hour. The genus name *Dendrolagus* comes from Greek words signifying "tree hare."

FAMILY
Macropodidae
RANGE
Southeastern New Guinea
HABITAT
Montane rain forest
SIZE
HB 22 to 30 inches (55 to 77 cm);
T 28 to 33 inches (70 to 85 cm);
W 13 to 22 pounds (6 to 10 kg)
LIFE CYCLE
Mating season not well defined; gestation about 32 days, one young born

SUGAR GLIDER / *Petaurus breviceps*

The sugar glider is named for its ability to sail through the air and its fondness for sweet tree sap. It can glide up to 165 feet (50 m), changing position in midair by moving its wrists and ankles to adjust its gliding membrane. Its regular diet includes insects, blossoms, and small vertebrates. It particularly enjoys the sap of wattle and gum trees, stripping off the bark with its incisors to reach its treat. A single tree can supply enough carbohydrates to feed a family of seven to twelve gliders for up to a year; the tree and neighboring sap-producing trees, rather than the territory itself, will be defended. Sugar gliders build nests in tree cavities, lining them with leaves that they carry with their tails.

FAMILY
Petauridae
RANGE
Eastern coast of Australia, New Guinea, and associated islands
HABITAT
Eucalyptus forest
SIZE
HB 6 to 8 inches (16 to 21 cm); T 6 to 8 inches (16 to 21 cm); W 3.5 to 7 ounces (100 to 200 g)
LIFE CYCLE
Mating year-round; gestation about 16 days, usually two young born that stay in mother's pouch up to 70 days

LEADBEATER'S POSSUM / *Gymnobelideus leadbeateri*

Sole species in the genus, *Gymnobelideus, leadbeateri* is believed by some researchers to be related to the sugar glider *(above)*—although it has no gliding capabilities, but instead jumps from branch to branch using its tail as a stabilizer. It builds its nests of bark high up in the hollows of mountain-ash trees and feeds on insects that it finds under the bark. For years this species was known to science by only a few specimens that had been collected before 1910. It was thought to be extinct until 1961, when several individuals were seen in the wild.

FAMILY
Petauridae
RANGE
Eastern coast of Australia
HABITAT
Eucalyptus forest
SIZE
HB 6 to 7 inches (15 to 17 cm); T 7.5 to 8 inches (19 to 20 cm); W 3.5 to 7 ounces (100 to 200 g)
LIFE CYCLE
Mating year-round, except December and January; gestation 15 to 17 days, one to two young born

STRIPED POSSUM / *Dactylopsila trivirgata*

The striped possum is so-named for its eye-catching black and white stripes. It takes shelter in tree cavities and hollow logs during the day and it comes out at night to forage for food. To locate its preferred staple, insects and their larvae, it taps on fallen logs. When it hears a hollow sound, the possum cuts into the wood with its sharp incisors and, using its elongated fourth digit and hooked claw, it removes the insects. These possums also feed on leaves and fruits. They mark their territory with long-lasting anal-gland secretions that smell like that of the similarly patterned skunk. However, instead of spraying it, the striped possum deposits the secretion directly on the contact surface.

FAMILY
Petauridae
RANGE
New Guinea, northeast Australia
HABITAT
Tropical rain forest

SIZE
HB 9 to 12 inches (23 to 30 cm); T 12 to 13 inches (31 to 34 cm); W 9 to 14 ounces (250 to 400 g)
LIFE CYCLE
Little is known; one or two young born

VESTED ANTEATER / *Tamandua mexicana*

This species uses its large, powerful claws to tear open ant and termite mounds, then laps up the insects with the long, sticky tongue that protrudes from its tiny mouth—less than half an inch (1 cm) in diameter. Since it is toothless, the insects are ground up in a part of its stomach that resembles a gizzard. Its prehensile tail has a hairless portion on the underside for gripping branches; it is often used as a fifth limb for climbing. When threatened, the anteater raises up on its hind limbs, hissing, its heavily clawed fore limbs extended, ready to do battle. The claws are so long that when the anteater walks, it treads on the sides of its paws. It cannot run.

FAMILY
Myrmecophagidae
RANGE
Southern Mexico
to South America
HABITAT
Tropical rain forest
and deciduous forest
SIZE
HB 21 to 23 inches (54 to 58 cm); T 21 to 22 inches (54 to 55.5 cm); W 8 to 13 pounds (3.5 to 6 kg)
LIFE CYCLE
Gestation 130 to 150 days; one young born in spring

BROWN-THROATED THREE-TOED SLOTH / *Bradypus variegatus*

Commonly mistaken for a primate, sloths are actually more closely related to the armadillo *(page 100)*. They are well known for their slow movement and metabolism, taking up to a month to digest a single meal of their preferred food: the leaves and fruit of trumpetwood. They are strictly arboreal, wrapping their long curved claws around branches as they move through the canopy to forage for leaves, flowers, and buds. They may be seen hanging from branches or sitting in the forks of trees, descending to the ground only to defecate or to crawl to another tree. A blue-green algae grows on their hair, providing camouflage *(page 10)*. Their distinctive "aye-aye" cry is heard more frequently during mating season. The three-toed sloth moves much slower than the its cousin the two-toed sloth *(Choloepus didactylus)*. All sloths are seriously threatened by large-scale clearing of forests in northern and eastern South America.

FAMILY
Bradypodidae
RANGE
Central America to Argentina
HABITAT
Evergreen and semi-deciduous forest
SIZE
HB 20 to 21 inches (50 to 54 cm); T 1.5 to 2 inches (4 to 5 cm); W 8 to 9 pounds (3.5 to 4 kg)
LIFE CYCLE
Mating year-round; gestation about 150 days, one young born

 MOONRAT / *Echinosorex gymnura*

One of the largest living members of the order Insectivora, the moonrat is most active at night, when it feeds on a variety of animals, including amphibians, beetles, roaches, termites, and insect larvae. Sometimes it also eats fruit. A good swimmer, the moonrat may take refuge in the water when threatened. In defense and to mark territory, it produces secretions, variously described as smelling of onion or rotten garlic. It is also called Raffle's moonrat or Raffle's gymnure, after Stanford Raffle, the zoologist who discovered it.

FAMILY
Erinaceidae
RANGE
Burma, Thailand, Malaysia, Indonesia
HABITAT
Tropical lowlands and forested foothills
SIZE
HB 10 to 18 inches (25 to 45 cm); T 6 to 12 inches (16 to 30 cm); W 1 to 3 pounds (0.5 to 1.4 kg)

LIFE CYCLE
Mating year-round; gestation 35 to 40 days, two young born

GIANT OTTER SHREW / *Potamogale velox*

A large member of the order Insectivora, *Potamogale velox* bears a superficial resemblance to an otter. Solitary and nocturnal, it spends most of its active time hunting to satisfy its

voracious appetite. When searching for food, it propels itself through the water with its flattened tail, using its whiskers to sense the presence of prey—mostly fish, but also freshwater invertebrates, especially crabs and mollusks. The food is taken ashore to be eaten. The giant otter shrew seldom eats amphibians, perhaps because it is sensitive to the noxious secretions in their skin. It usually makes its burrows under or adjacent to a tree, with the entrance close to the trunk above the water line.

FAMILY
Tenrecidae
RANGE
Central equatorial Africa to Ivory Coast
HABITAT
Tropical rivers, streams, and swamps
SIZE
HB 11 to 14 inches (29 to 35 cm);
T 9 to 11 inches (24 to 29 cm);
W about 1 pound (0.5 kg)
LIFE CYCLE
Believed to mate year-round;
one to three young born

HAITIAN SOLENODON / *Solenodon paradoxus*

During the day this slow-moving creature lives in small family groups that shelter in caves, rock crevices, and hollowed-out logs. At night, it forages for food, ripping open rotting logs and rustling through leaf litter, probably relying on its sense of smell to seek out reptiles, insects, grubs, fruit, and other plant matter. It can eat a small reptile or a large beetle without fear of

injuring itself by first immobilizing the prey with poisonous saliva, which runs down a grooved incisor and is injected by biting. A rare and endangered species, the Haitian solenodon is increasingly at risk due to deforestation, urbanization, and the introduction of exotic mammalian predators. Its natural predators are birds of prey and snakes.

FAMILY
Solenodontidae
RANGE
Hispaniola
HABITAT
Tropical wooded areas with brushy and rocky terrain
SIZE
HB 11 to 13 inches (28 to 33 cm); T 7 to 10 inches (17 to 25 cm); W 1.5 to 2.2 pounds (0.7 to 1 kg)
LIFE CYCLE
Little is known; gestation in captivity about 64 days, one young born

COMMON TREE SHREW / *Tupaia glis*

The name "tree shrew" is a misnomer since—aside from its long nose and insatiable appetite—*Tupaia glis* is quite different from the true shrew in the order Insectivora. A diurnal species, *T. glis* spends its waking hours hunting for insects, fruit, and seeds among leaf litter. Some scientists believe it is an ancestor of the primates, others that it is related to the insectivores. Because of the debate it has been placed in its own order, Scandentia. The genus name comes from the Malay word *tupai*, which means "squirrel."

FAMILY
Tupaiidae
RANGE
Southeast Asia
HABITAT
Tropical forests and shrubby areas

SIZE
HB 5 to 7 inches (12.5 to 18.5 cm);
T 5.5 to 7 inches (14 to 17 cm);
W 2 to 6 ounces (50 to 180 g)
LIFE CYCLE
Mating when conditions favorable; gestation 40 to 52 days, one to three young born

COLUGO / *Cynocephalus variegatus*

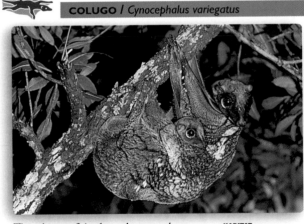

The colugo, or flying lemur, has a membrane that extends from its neck to the tips of its fingers and toes and encloses the tail. When stretched, this membrane enables it to glide from tree to tree. It can glide over distances of more than 300 feet (100 m). It is strictly arboreal and cannot move easily on the ground. It sleeps by day in hollow trees, emerging at dusk and gliding along a well-established route to a feeding tree. It eats fruits, buds, flowers, and shoots and may drink the sap of certain trees. This unusual mammal lives alone, but several may feed at the same tree. If disturbed, it makes a rasping cry. The female wraps her tiny baby in the gliding membrane and may carry it with her when foraging.

FAMILY
Cynocephalidae
RANGE
Southeast Asia
HABITAT
Tropical forests from lowlands to highlands
SIZE
HB 13 to 16.5 inches (34 to 42 cm);
T 8 to 10 inches (20 to 25 cm);
W 2 to 4 pounds (1 to 2 kg)
LFE CYCLE
Mating January to April; gestation 60 days, one young (rarely twins) born

HAMMER-HEAD BAT / *Hypsignathus monstrosus*

This fruit bat is the largest in Africa. The female has a head shaped like that of a flying fox. The male has a hammer-shaped muzzle that may help to amplify its voice; he also has a voice box that fills most of his chest cavity. In mating periods, the males congregate at traditional mating sites, set up small territories, and make loud "kwoks" to attract the females. During these sessions, the males call all night, often in chorus, broadcasting every second or two. Outside of the mating season, these bats roam about singly or in small groups, foraging at night among fruiting trees and roosting by day in the foliage.

FAMILY
Pteropodidae
RANGE
West and central Africa, west to Kenya, south to Angola
HABITAT
Lowland swamps, mangroves, and wet areas
SIZE
HB 7.5 to 12 inches (19 to 30 cm);
FA 5 to 5.5 inches (12 to 14 cm);
W 7 to 16 ounces (200 to 450 g)
LIFE CYCLE
Mating depends on locale; gestation 160 to 170 days, one young born

TOME'S SWORD-NOSED BAT / *Lonchorhina aurita*

These bats, like others of the family Phyllostomidae, have a leaflike projection on the tip of their nose and so are called leaf-nosed bats. All four species in this genus have particularly long leaf-noses, but *Lonchorhina aurita* has the largest of all: Some have "sword-noses" longer than 3 inches (6 cm)—about the same size as their large ears. The function of the sword-nose is unclear, but it is believed to aid in echolocation. These bats display amazing maneuverability as they move through the forest understory and glean insects from vegetation. By day they roost in caves and hollow trees along with about twenty individuals, although larger groups of up to five hundred individuals have been observed.

FAMILY
Phyllostomidae
RANGE
Mexico to southeastern Brazil
HABITAT
Tropical forest
SIZE
HB 2.1 to 2.7 inches (5.3 to 6.8 cm);
T 1.6 to 2.5 inches (4.2 to 6.5 cm);
FA 1.9 to 2.2 inches (4.8 to 5.5 cm);
W 0.4 to 0.6 ounce (12 to 16 g)
LIFE CYCLE
Mating during rainy season from December to April; one young born

FALSE VAMPIRE BAT / *Vampyrum spectrum*

The largest bat in the New World and the only species in its genus, *Vampyrum spectrum* was once thought to drink blood. It is now known to feed instead on rodents, birds, and occasionally insects, as well as other bats—hence the word "false" in its common name. The bats capture mice by pouncing on them and breaking their neck, back, or skull. They grasp birds by the beak and crush the skull with their teeth. Food is usually taken to a roost to be eaten. Unlike most bats, they are believed to pair-bond. The male has been observed folding its wings around the female and young while nesting by day, presumably to aid in heat retention. They roost in small groups, usually in hollow trees or snags. Habitat destruction seriously threatens the species.

FAMILY
Phyllostomidae
RANGE
Southern Mexico to Peru
and Brazil; Trinidad

HABITAT
Tropical forest
SIZE
HB 5 to 5.3 inches (12.5 to 13.5 cm);
FA 4 to 4.3 inches (10 to 11 cm);
W 5 to 7 ounces (150 to 200 g)
LIFE CYCLE
Little is known; in captivity, one young born in June

COMMON TENT-MAKING BAT / *Uroderma bilobatus*

This bat has a fleshy flap of skin on its nose and so is grouped with the other leaf-nosed bats in the family Phyllostomidae. It has yellow ear margins and four white facial stripes. It is called the tent-making bat because it bites rows of small holes in large broad leaves, causing their structure to weaken and their edges to sag, forming a protective "tent." Although an individual may be found under its own tent, it is more common to find small colonies of twenty to thirty. A leaf tent can be used for up to two months before it needs to be replaced. An important pollinator, this bat feeds on pollen and nectar, as well as insects and the juice of tropical fruits.

FAMILY
Phyllostomidae
RANGE
Southern Mexico to southeastern Brazil
HABITAT
Tropical forest
SIZE
HB 2 to 3 inches (5.5 to 7.5 cm);
FA about 1.5 inches (3.7 cm);
W 0.5 to 0.8 ounce (13 to 22 g)
LIFE CYCLE
Mating depends on locale;
one young born

JAMAICAN FRUIT-EATING BAT / *Artibeus jamaicensis*

These leaf-nosed bats have a highly organized social system. The older males control large harems that may contain more than twenty females. Groups of males and non-reproductive females, as well as pregnant and lactating females, also occur. When one of the bats in a foraging group becomes caught by a predator, it emits a high-pitched distress signal, calling the others of the group to come and mob the attacker. These bats are important disseminators of seeds because the fruit that they eat passes through their digestive system in only about fifteen minutes—too quickly for the seeds to be digested.

FAMILY
Phyllostomidae
RANGE
Florida keys; Mexico to Brazil and northwestern Argentina; West Indies
HABITAT
Tropical forest
SIZE
HB 3 to 3.5 inches (7.5 to 9 cm);
FA 2.4 to 2.8 inches (6 to 7 cm);
W 1.4 to 2.5 ounces (40 to 70 g)

LIFE CYCLE
Mating year-round depending on locale, peak February to July; implantation and development delayed, usually one young born

GREATER FISHING BAT / *Noctilio leporinus*

This bat "fishes" using echolocation to sense the ripples made by fish breaking the water. Once it has located the presence of a fish, it swoops down and grabs the meal with its long, curved claws. If the fish is small, it is eaten in flight; larger fish are carried back to a roost. Aquatic crustaceans, beetles, and other insects are also included in the fishing bat's diet. Occasionally, one of these bats will miss its prey and crash into the water. It then has to paddle to shore with its wings. These bats often roost in groups of fifty or more in a hollow tree, cave, or crevice, easily located because of their strong, musky odor.

FAMILY
Noctilionidae
RANGE
Western and southern Mexico to Argentina and Brazil; West Indies
HABITAT
Tropical forest near water
SIZE
HB 4 to 5 inches (10 to 13 cm);
FA 3 to 3.5 inches (7 to 9 cm);
W 1.4 to 2.9 ounces (40 to 83 g)
LIFE CYCLE
Mating probably September to December; gestation about 112 days, one young born

WHITE-HANDED GIBBON / *Hylobates lar*

Although sometimes referred to as the common lar or lar gibbon, this long-limbed, tail-less primate sports white fur on its hands and feet and hence is more popularly known as the white-handed gibbon. True brachiators, gibbons move faster and display greater agility than any other group of primates. Primatologists jokingly refer to them as "real swingers." They can reach speeds of up to thirty-one miles (50 km) per hour and hurl themselves some forty feet (12 m) from branch to branch. They live in small family groups and forage together on shoots, leaves, fruit, buds, flowers, and occasionally insects. Different forms of the white-handed gibbon vary in their color and calls, depending on the geographic location.

FAMILY
Hylobatidae
RANGE
Southeast Asia and China
HABITAT
Tropical evergreen to tropical dry forest
SIZE
HB 18 to 25 inches (45 to 63 cm);
W 11 to 18 pounds (5 to 8 kg)

LIFE CYCLE
Gestation 200 to 212 days, usually
one young born

GORILLA / *Gorilla gorilla*

These peaceful animals—the largest of the primates—spend their days eating leaves, herbs, fruit, roots, and sometimes bark. They are usually found in groups of five to ten individuals, made up of several females, their young, and a dominant male—known as the silverback because of the silvery hair on his back that develops as he reaches maturity. When attacked or to scare off a rival, the male stands tall and screams as he beats his chest. Sometimes he charges and rips up vegetation, which he throws into the air. There are three subspecies of *Gorilla gorilla* and all are endangered because of habitat destruction and hunters who sell the young alive as pets and adults dead for food and good-luck charms.

FAMILY
Hominidae
RANGE
Central Africa
HABITAT
Openings in tropical forest
SIZE
HB 5 to 6 feet (1.5 to 1.8 m); W 265 to 500 pounds (120 to 227 kg)
LIFE CYCLE
Mating year-round; gestation 250 to 270 days, one young born

INDRI / *Indri indri*

The largest surviving lemur, this arboreal vegetarian stays in the deep forest, foraging during the day for leaves, fruit, flowers, bulbs, and, when resources are scarce, bark and dead wood. The indri has a specialized throat sac that

enables it to emit loud howls and shrill cries, which can be heard for up to two miles (3 km). These vocalizations serve to keep individuals in contact and to delineate individual territories. Indri are sensitive to human-made sound, which can disrupt their ability to reproduce. Their Malagasy name *babakoto* means "father of man," reflecting their place in traditional Malagasy concepts about human origins. Local taboos against killing the indri have helped to protect it in the past, but recent hunting by outsiders and, more importantly, loss of habitat pose a serious threat to the indri's survival.

FAMILY
Indridae
RANGE
Northeastern Madagascar
HABITAT
Coastal and montane rain forests
SIZE
HB 24 to 35 inches (60 to 90 cm);
T 2 to 2.4 inches (5 to 6 cm); W 15
to 22 pounds (7 to 10 kg)
LIFE CYCLE
Gestation 120 to 150 days, usually
one young born

MANDRILL / *Mandrillus sphinx*

Males of this species are well known for their brightly colored face, buttocks, and genitals. Females are smaller and less colorful. They spend most of the day foraging on the ground in open areas, eating fruit, buds, leaves, insects, and fungi. At night or when threatened, they retreat to the forest canopy. Social primates, mandrills are typically found in groups of twenty to forty, usually led by an older male. The young are often seen riding on the mother's back or clinging to the fur on her belly. Changes in land use and hunting threaten the species.

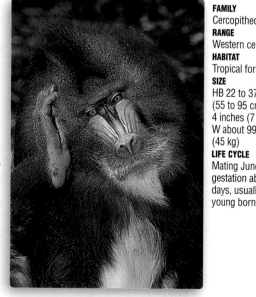

FAMILY
Cercopithecidae
RANGE
Western central Africa
HABITAT
Tropical forest
SIZE
HB 22 to 37 inches
(55 to 95 cm); T 3 to
4 inches (7 to 10 cm);
W about 99 pounds
(45 kg)
LIFE CYCLE
Mating June to August;
gestation about 170
days, usually one
young born

COTTON-TOP TAMARIN / *Saguinus oedipus*

This New World primate is easily distinguished by the crest of white hair on its black head. When it stands on its hindlegs in an aggressive display, these hairs sometimes become erect. The cotton-top tamarin is arboreal and forages by day, eating fruit, insects, and small vertebrates such as mice and birds. It lives in groups of three to thirteen. One of its many vocalizations is a warning whistle that serves to alert others of an aerial predator. Both sexes help care for the young, and two weeks after birth, the father becomes the primary parent to carry the offspring about. Siblings also help out, affording them a chance to practice parenting skills.

FAMILY
Callithricidae
RANGE
Northern Colombia
HABITAT
Lowland tropical evergreen forest
SIZE
HB 8 to 9.5 inches (21 to 24 cm); T 13 to 16 inches (33 to 40 cm); W about 1 pound (0.5 kg)
LIFE CYCLE
Mating January to February; gestation 140 to 145 days, usually two young born

TARSIER / *Tarsius syrichta*

The tarsier's name comes from its elongated tarsal (ankle) bones, which allow it to jump quickly. At night this nocturnal creature forages in the lower levels of the forest canopy, hopping to the ground to catch crickets, lizards, snakes, ants, and scorpions. Its large eyes lack cones in the retina, nor does it have a reflecting tapetum *(page 47)*, suggesting that it may have evolved from diurnal ancestors. It cannot move its eyes well and so must rotate its head in order to look around. Once the tarsier catches its prey in its hand, it kills the victim by biting it several times. This rat-sized mammal usually lives in pairs, and spends the day sleeping, clinging to tree trunks, stems, or stalks. After a long gestation, the female gives birth to a large offspring, weighing up to 30 percent of her weight.

FAMILY
Tarsiidae
RANGE
Southeastern Philippines
HABITAT
Lowland and coastal forest
SIZE
HB 5 to 5.5 inches (12 to 14 cm); T 8 to 9 inches (21 to 23 cm); W 3.5 to 5.3 ounces (100 to 150 g)
LIFE CYCLE
Mating throughout year; gestation about 180 days, one young born

BALD UAKARI / *Cacajao calvus*

Little is known about the bald uakari. A diurnal species, it is almost totally arboreal and spends much of its time high in the rain-forest canopy searching for fruit, insects, and small vertebrates to eat. It rarely makes a noise and thus can move through the forest without being detected, even

when traveling in groups. The groups are a mix of fifteen to thirty males, females, and their young. There are two species of uakari, *Cacajao calvus* and *C. melanocephalus*, both of which possess a wrinkled red face and a bald head. *C. calvus* has four subspecies; the one shown here is called the red uakari because of its reddish brown to chestnut coat. All uakari are threatened because of logging, mining, and agriculture in their habitat, activities that have also provided access roads for hunters who kill them for food and sell them young as pets.

FAMILY
Cebidae
RANGE
Upper Amazon basin
HABITAT
Flooded forests, river edges,
and swamps
SIZE
HB 20 to 22 inches (51 to 57 cm);
T about 6 inches (15.5 cm);
W 7 to 11 pounds (3 to 5 kg)
LIFE CYCLE
Unknown in wild

BINTURONG / *Arctictis binturong*

The binturong has a long shaggy coat and looks like a little bear with tufted ears. It is one of two species in the order Carnivora—the other is the kinkajou *(page opposite)*—with a prehensile tail, used along with non-retractable claws to grasp branches as it moves slowly through the trees. The binturong's movement is often accompanied by guttural grunts and hissing sounds. By day it sleeps in a tree; its nights are devoted to foraging for fruit, plants, insects, and small animals. It has also been seen diving into water and swimming to catch fish.

FAMILY
Viverridae
RANGE
Southeast Asia
HABITAT
Dense tropical and subtropical forest

SIZE
HB 24 to 38 inches (61 to 96 cm); T 22
to 35 inches (56 to 89 cm); W 20 to 30
pounds (9 to 14 kg)
LIFE CYCLE
Mating peaks March to April and October
to November; gestation 84 to 99 days,
one to six young born

BLOTCHED GENET / *Genetta tigrina*

About the size of a large house cat, this attractive carnivore is mainly nocturnal and solitary in its habits. During the day it sleeps in a vine tangle, on a branch, or in a hole in the ground. Each individual has a well-defined territory that it marks with strong-smelling secretions from the perineal glands or with urine. It is a good climber and can descend trees head-first. It eats mainly rodents, but will also consume invertebrates and fruit. The blotched genet hunts on the ground, ambushing and quickly running down its prey. It is usually silent in the wild, but it can make a variety of catlike calls, coughs, and screams. This genet is found in tropical forests, but it adapts well to other habitats and also occurs in agricultural areas,

swamps, and villages. It is widespread and not endangered.

FAMILY
Viverridae
RANGE
Most of sub-Saharan Africa
HABITAT
Tropical forests, mixed woodland, swamps, and tall grass
SIZE
HB 16 to 22 inches (40 to 55 cm); T 16 to 22 inches (40 to 55 cm); W 2 to 7 pounds (1 to 3 kg)
LIFE CYCLE
Gestation about 70 days; two to five young born that stay with mother for six months and can breed at one year of age

KINKAJOU / *Potos flavus*

This arboreal species, also known as the honey bear (a reference to its golden fur, not to its taste for honey), has a prehensile tail like the binturong *(page opposite)*. An agile climber, it uses its tail as a fifth limb, freeing up its hands to hold food items. It spends most of its days sleeping or resting inside a hollow tree, coming out only at night to forage. Its diet consists of insects, small vertebrates such as birds, fruit, and nectar, which it laps up with its long tongue. When the kinkajou is attacked, it fights back, grasping the predator with its limbs and tail and repeatedly biting with its strong canines.

FAMILY
Procyonidae
RANGE
Southern Mexico to Brazil
HABITAT
All types of tropical forests, wet and dry

SIZE
HB 16 to 22 inches (41 to 57 cm); T 16 to 22 inches (40 to 56 cm); W 4 to 10 pounds (2 to 5 kg)
LIFE CYCLE
Mating throughout year; gestation 112 to 118 days; one (rarely two) young born

JAGUAR / *Panthera onca*

One of the largest members in the family Felidae, the jaguar is a proficient hunter of a variety of small and large vertebrates on the ground and in the trees. Highly territorial over an extensive home range of up to about eighty square miles (200 sq km), it lives a solitary life—except during the breeding season, when male and female come together to mate and repro-

duce. After the young are born, the female becomes highly aggressive toward any perceived threat—which can include the father. The young may stay with the mother for up to two years as they hone their hunting skills. Hunting for sport and pelt are the primary reasons for the decline of this species, although deforestation and habitat loss have contributed as well.

FAMILY
Felidae
RANGE
Mexico, Central America
into South America
HABITAT
Tropical and subtropical forests; open woodlands, swamps, and savannas
SIZE
HB 4 to 6 feet (1.2 to 1.8 m); T 18 to 30 inches (45 to 75 cm); SH about 28 inches (70 cm); W 77 to 350 pounds (35 to 160 kg)
LIFE CYCLE
Mating year-round in some locales, in spring in cooler regions; gestation 90 to 110 days, one to four cubs born

GIANT OTTER / *Pteronura brasiliensis*

The giant otter's flattened tail, sharp claws, and long webbed toes enable it to move easily through the water, feeding on fish and crustaceans—consuming up to nine pounds (4 kg) of food a day. A diurnal species, it can sometimes be heard uttering shrill cries, purrs, and

whistlelike calls. Groups of four to eight individuals sleep together in chambered burrows dug in the river bank. The species is threatened through habitat loss and, although protected by law, "the waterdog," as it is called, is still hunted for its meat and pelt.

FAMILY
Mustelidae
RANGE
Northern and eastern South America
HABITAT
Slow-moving rivers and lagoons in forested regions
SIZE
HB 35 to 55 inches (90 to 140 cm); T 19 to 28 inches (50 to 70 cm); W 48 to 71 pounds (22 to 32 kg)
LIFE CYCLE
Mating June to August; gestation 65 to 70 days, usually two or three young born

BOUTU / *Inia geoffrensis*

The boutu is also called the pink river dolphin because of the pinkish hue of its skin. The eyes of the boutu (and other river dolphins) are reduced because the rivers in which it lives are murky and visibility is poor. Instead the boutu utilizes echolocation to help it find fish for food and to avoid obstacles. Traditionally the human inhabitants of the Amazon basin believed that the boutu possesses supernatural powers and there are many local myths relating to its charm, beauty, and sexuality. Consequently, native peoples have rarely hunted it, except for use in medicines and aphrodisiacs. Today, however, this species is under seige. Fishing nets trap the boutus, agricultural chemicals poison them, and their overall habitat is being seriously disrupted by expanding human population and the building of hydroelectric dams. Other species of river dolphins occur elsewhere in South America and in Asia.

FAMILY
Platanistidae
RANGE
Upper Amazon basin
and upper Orinoco River
HABITAT
Freshwater rivers, streams,
and lakes
SIZE
TL 5 to 8 feet (1.6 to 2.5 m);
W 154 to 353 pounds (70 to 160 kg)
LIFE CYCLE
Mating June to September;
gestation 305 to 335 days,
one calf born

BAIRD'S TAPIR / *Tapirus bairdii*

As with other tapirs, the short trunk of the Baird's tapir is composed of nose and upper lip. The tapir uses its trunk to pick up grasses, leaves, and fruit and carry them to the mouth. This elusive creature is an important seed disseminator because it prefers to spit out fruit seeds rather than eat them along with the flesh. Although it spends most of its time in the water or lying in the mud, the tapir can move quickly and is an excellent swimmer. The Baird's tapir is easy to track because it often follows previously used paths and it leaves distinctive three-toed tracks (each toe has a broad hoof). The species was heavily hunted for sport, its meat, and its hide; today it is also threatened by deforestation for agriculture and logging.

FAMILY
Tapiridae
RANGE
Southern Mexico to northern Colombia
HABITAT
Tropical forests, often near streams
SIZE
HB 6.5 to 8 feet (2 to 2.4 m) ;T 3 to 5 inches (7 to 13 cm); SH 36 to 47 inches (91 to 120 cm); W 551 to 661 pounds (250 to 300 kg)
LIFE CYCLE
Mating year-round; gestation 390 to 405 days, one calf (rarely two) born

RED RIVER HOG / *Potamochoerus porcus*

Also called the bush or red river pig, this species lives in groups of up to forty individuals, each led by an older male. Sometimes when two different groups meet, they exhibit ritualized threats. The display, however, rarely intensifies into serious fighting. These hogs will eat almost anything and can cause extensive damage to agricultural crops. They use their long snout as a plow, tearing up vegetation as they search the subsoil for roots and tubers. Their natural predators tend to be species such as leopards that require an extremely large range to survive and are becoming rare. Therefore, despite being hunted by humans, the population of the red river hog today exceeds normal levels.

FAMILY
Suidae
RANGE
Sub-Saharan Africa and Madagascar

HABITAT
Dense tropical forest
SIZE
HB 3 to 5 feet (1 to 1.5 m); T 12 to 18 inches (30 to 45 cm); SH 25 to 30 inches (64 to 75 cm); W 120 to 181 pounds (54.5 to 82 kg)
LIFE CYCLE
Mating throughout year; gestation 120 to 130 days, usually three or four young born

OKAPI / *Okapia johnstoni*

This reclusive diurnal species lives in some of the densest parts of the rain forest. Although it has long been hunted by indigenous pygmy tribes, it was discovered by the outside world only in 1901. At first it was thought to be related to the zebra because of its black- and white-striped flanks, but it is now known to be a member of the giraffe family. The males have small, hairy, backward-pointing horns and both sexes have extremely long tongues, which they use to clean their eyes and to manipulate leaves, fruit, plants, and shoots as they eat. The young are often left alone hidden in the thick forest, but at any hint of danger, the mother will run to her calf and fiercely beat her front feet on the ground as she faces the threat.

FAMILY
Giraffidae
RANGE
Northeastern Zaire
HABITAT
Dense forest
SIZE
HB 4 to 6.6 feet (1.2 to 2 m); T 12 to 16.5 inches (30 to 42 cm); W 463 to 551 pounds (210 to 250 kg)
LIFE CYCLE
Mating throughout year, peaks May to June and November to December; gestation 421 to 457 days, usually one calf born

SPOTTED MOUSE DEER / *Moschiola meminna*

Preyed on by various carnivores, large snakes, and humans, spotted mouse deer tend to be reclusive and timid. They enjoy a measure of protection from the white speckling on their brown fur, which breaks up their outline and offers them camouflage. These miniature deer create tunnel-like trails through the undergrowth, which they follow when foraging for leaves, shoots, buds, and fruit to eat. The males have long, sharp upper canines that they put to use when fighting other males over territory and females. Their battles begin with them charging each other. Once engaged, they repeatedly bite the rival all over.

FAMILY
Tragulidae
RANGE
Southern India and Sri Lanka
HABITAT
Tropical forest
SIZE
HB 18.5 to 23 inches (47 to 58 cm); T 1 to 2 inches (3 to 5 cm); SH 10 to 12 inches (25 to 30 cm); W 5 to 6 pounds (2.2 to 2.7 kg)
LIFE CYCLE
Little is known; gestation believed to be 140 to 170 days, one young born

TREE PANGOLIN / *Manis tricuspis*

All pangolins possess large overlapping scales; those of the tree pangolin have three points on each scale—hence its species name, *tricuspis*. The pangolin uses its long prehensile tail to help it climb in search of ant and termite nests. It rips nests apart with its arms, then laps up the insects with its extremely long tongue. Its armor does not protect it from being bitten; the insects crawl under the scales and bite its skin. However, the insects are crushed between the scales when the pangolin moves. If threatened by a predator, the pangolin rolls into a ball until it looks like a giant pine cone.

FAMILY
Manidae
RANGE
Sub-Saharan Africa
HABITAT
Tropical forest
SIZE
HB 14 to 18 inches (35 to 45 cm); T 19 to 24 inches (49 to 60 cm); W 4 to 5 pounds (1.8 to 2.4 kg)

LIFE CYCLE
Gestation 120 to 150 days, one young born

CUVIER'S FIRE-FOOTED TREE SQUIRREL / *Funisciurus pyrropus*

Cuvier's tree squirrel is primarily an arboreal species. However, it forages for food—fruit, seeds, plants, insects, eggs, and small vertebrates—on the ground. It may sometimes be seen at dawn or dusk, foraging in pairs in forest clearings and sometimes in secondary forests, riparian areas, and coastal and mangrove forests. During the hotter parts of the day, it retires to its nest of leaves, which it constructs in an axil of a palm tree. It is preyed on primarily by snakes, genets, and predatory birds.

FAMILY
Sciuridae
RANGE
Central and eastern Africa
HABITAT
Tropical woodlands and palm stands
SIZE
HB 5 to 11 inches (13 to 27 cm); T 4 to 8 inches (10 to 20 cm); W about 1 pound (0.5 kg)
LIFE CYCLE
Poorly known; gestation probably 21 to 42 days, two or three young born

PACA / *Agouti paca*

The paca is a large nocturnal rodent. Strong and agile, it can jump up to about seven feet (2 m) high. Spotted flanks help it blend in with the vegetation. It has an inflated cranium that enables it to make very loud sounds, presumably in territorial disputes. It feeds primarily on fruit and may be an important disseminator of seeds by leaving behind seed-rich feces. It also eats leaves, roots, and twigs. During the day, the paca shelters in a burrow, which it has either dug

itself or taken over from another mammal and modified. Burrow entrances are located among tree roots or rocks or along river banks, and are usually sealed from the inside and well camouflaged with leaves. The dens themselves are lined with plant material. The paca is considered a food delicacy by many peoples.

FAMILY
Agoutidae
RANGE
Southern Mexico to Brazil
HABITAT
Forested areas near water
SIZE
HB 24 to 31 inches (60 to 79 cm); T 1 to 2 inches (2 to 5 cm); W 14 to 26 pounds (6 to 12 kg)
LIFE CYCLE
Poorly known; gestation about 116 days, one young born

PREHENSILE-TAILED PORCUPINE / *Coendou prehensilis*

This porcupine shelters during the day high in the forest canopy and in tree cavities and rarely descends to the ground. It uses its partly hairless, callused prehensile tail for balance and to grip branches while it eats leaves, shoots, fresh twigs, and fruit at night. Each digit on its hind and fore limbs has a long curved claw to aid in climbing. Adults are covered with a protective coat of hard and pointed spines; the young are born with a softer coat that soon hardens. The size of the home range may be large, but varies depending on the season. When individuals are separated, they may contact each other with long moaning sounds.

FAMILY
Erethizontidae
RANGE
South America
HABITAT
Tropical forest
SIZE
HB 12 to 24 inches (30 to 60 cm); T 13 to 18 inches (33 to 45 cm); W 2 to 11 pounds (1 to 5 kg)
LIFE CYCLE
Poorly known; gestation 195 to 210 days, one young born

GOLDEN-RUMPED ELEPHANT-SHREW / *Rhynchocyon chrysopygus*

This species is named after the color of its rear end and its long snout. A terrestrial insectivore, it has never been observed climbing or burrowing. Every few nights, it constructs a new sleeping nest—a shallow depression lined and then concealed with leaves. These animals form pairs, and both sexes mark and defend their territory. They vocalize with squeals and squeaks, and frequently appear agitated. Their diet is composed primarily of insects, but they also eat small birds, birds' eggs, and smaller mammals. They are seriously threatened by habitat loss.

FAMILY
Macroscelididae
RANGE
Coastal Kenya
HABITAT
Patches of coastal forest and scrubland

SIZE
HB 9 to 12 inches (23 to 30 cm); T 7 to 10 inches (20 to 25 cm); W about 1 pound (0.5 kg)
LIFE CYCLE
Mating year-round; gestation about 42 days, one or two young born

Tropical Grassland & Savanna

During dry winter months, tropical grasslands *(map, pages 84 to 85)* grow parched and their streams and pools dry up. With summer, however, comes rain, and the land is transformed by flourishing grasses and flowers.

Surprisingly, tropical grasslands are often found in regions with enough rainfall to support luxuriant tropical rain forests year-round. But extensive tree growth in these areas is discouraged by strong winds that blow across the flat land and by the fast-draining grassland soils. Where trees such as baobabs and acacias do grow, they tend to be scattered about; such grassland is called a savanna. Africa is renowned for savannas where giraffes *(page 127)* browse on trees almost twenty feet (6 m) high. Another browser, the African elephant *(page 122)*, munches on trees as well as bushes and grass. Scientists believe that the elephants may coordinate their eating patterns by signaling to each other in ultra-low pitches. At night during the dry season, these sounds can travel as far as twelve miles (20 km).

Other grassland wildlife includes zebras *(page 123)* and blackbucks *(page 126)*, ungulates that feed on grass and must cover vast distances in search of fresh green patches. Preying on these large herds of herbivores are carnivorous such as cheetahs *(page 121)*, lions *(page 121)*, hyenas, and hunting dogs.

The specialized feeding habits and preferences of most ungulates may reduce competition among species. For example, although herds of gnus *(page 125)* consume about 80 percent of the grass growing in their path across the Serengeti plain during their annual migration, by the time the herds of Thomson's gazelles *(page 126)* pass over the land a couple of months later, the grazed-over grass reveals fresh shoots— their preferred food.

During the dry season, the grasslands of northern Tanzania's Tarangire National Park are home to thousands of elephants, gnus, zebras, and other wildlife.

RED KANGAROO / *Macropus rufus*

The red kangaroo gets its name from the red pelage of the males—not the females, which tend to be dull blue-gray. The largest living marsupials in the world, these mammals use their tail as a balance when they jump; they can make jumps almost thirty feet (9 m) long and eight feet (2.5 m) high. They are active in the evening and at night, when groups of kangaroos, called mobs, forage on grasses and other plants. A mob usually has one adult male, several females, plus the young. Soon after giving birth, the mother copulates and produces an embryo that halts development until the neonate leaves the pouch. When conditions are right, she may have an "embryo-in-waiting," a suckling neonate, and a joey at her side.

FAMILY
Macropodidae
RANGE
Inland Australia
HABITAT
Arid grassland, shrubby steppes
SIZE
HB 3 to 5 feet (1 to 1.6 m); T 35 to 43 inches (90 to 110 cm); W 77 to 176 pounds (35 to 80 kg)
LIFE CYCLE
Mating year-round, implantation of embryo delayed until conditions suitable; gestation 30 to 40 days, one young born that stays in mother's pouch for 230 to 250 days

SOUTHERN HAIRY-NOSED WOMBAT / *Lasiorhinus latifrons*

Wombats live in an elaborate system of separate burrows that form a warren, with all entrances at the surface having paths that join them together. These are nocturnal marsupials, with pouches that open in the rear. Occasionally they can be seen coming out of their burrows in the early evening to feed predominantly on grass. The northern hairy-nosed wombat (*Lasiorhinus krefftii*), the only other species in this genus, is precariously close to extinction; it numbers less than one hundred individuals. Its decline has been linked to habitat loss, competition with grazing cattle, and human persecution. The habitat of the southern hairy-nosed wombat is now similarly under threat.

FAMILY
Vombatidae
RANGE
Coastal plain of south Australia
HABITAT
Grasslands to open woodlands
SIZE
HB 33 to 41 inches (85 to 104 cm); W up to 60 pounds (27 kg)
LIFE CYCLE
Mating September to November; gestation 20 to 22 days, one (rarely two) young born that stay in mother's pouch for up to 210 days

PICHI / *Zaedyus pichiy*

This common armadillo is often referred to as the hairy armadillo because of the hairs that grow from between its bony protective plates. Sharp claws and strong arms enable it to excavate shallow holes for shelter and short burrows in soft sand to sleep in. When these solitary animals come out to forage for insects, worms, and carrion, they depend on their well-developed sense of smell to lead them to the food. If the pichi feels threatened, it will quickly run away and dig itself a small hole. Once wedged inside, it pulls in its feet. The flesh of the pichi is considered to be tasty by the people of its region.

FAMILY
Dasypodidae
RANGE
Northern Argentina and Chile

HABITAT
Grassland and aridland
SIZE
HB 10 to 13 inches (26 to 33.5 cm); T 4 to 5 inches (10 to 12 cm); W 2 to 4 pounds (1 to 2 kg)
LIFE CYCLE
Believed to breed throughout year; gestation about 60 days, usually two young born

GELADA BABOON / *Theropithecus gelada*

These baboons, remarkable for their bright red, hairless chests and throats, spend their days foraging in alpine meadows, eating grasses along with their seeds and bulbs. At night they sleep on small ledges lining cliff walls. They live in large groups composed of up to four hundred individuals. Within these groups, social life focuses on smaller groups, which are typically made up of a single adult male and his harem of up to twelve females and their young. Although the male helps keep the group together through vocalizations and facial gestures, the females influence the mating process, with the more dominant ones having the best access to the males. This species is under threat due to habitat destruction and hunting.

FAMILY
Cercopithecidae
RANGE
Northern Ethiopia
HABITAT
Montane grassland and rocky areas
SIZE
HB 20 to 30 inches (50 to 75 cm); T 18 to 22 inches (45 to 55 cm); W 30 to 46 pounds (14 to 21 kg)
LIFE CYCLE
Mating May to July; gestation 147 to 192 days, one young (rarely twins) born

CHEETAH / *Acinonyx jubatus*

The cheetah can reach speeds of sixty-eight miles (110 km) per hour, making it the fastest mammal in the world. It has non-retractable claws (unlike those of other cats), which provide it with better traction when it runs on soft ground. Unlike most large cats, which hunt by ambush, the cheetah chases its prey at high speed, using its tail as a stabilizer, especially when making tight turns. It preys on many of the animals that share its habitat, including gazelles, gnus, antelopes, and warthogs. The males often live in small groups; the females are solitary, meeting up with males only to mate. Once hunted for its spotted coat, the cheetah is now protected. However, poaching and habitat destruction continue to threaten it.

FAMILY
Felidae
RANGE
Sub-Saharan Africa and isolated pockets in southwestern Asia
HABITAT
Savanna and open grassland
SIZE
HB about 5 feet (1.5 m); T 26 to 32 inches (65 to 80 cm); SH 27 to 34 inches (69 to 86 cm); W 88 to 143 pounds (40 to 65 kg)
LIFE CYCLE
Mating year-round, peaks August to December; gestation 90 to 95 days, one to eight cubs born

LION / *Panthera leo*

Social groups of lions, called prides, are composed of one to three males, two to fifteen females, and their offspring. Sometimes young males form their own satellite group. The males protect the territory and get to eat first; the lionesses do most of the hunting. They generally stalk and chase their prey, killing with a bite to the neck—although they can also kill with a single back-breaking swat of the paw. Lions usually hunt at night and spend almost twenty hours a day sleeping or lounging with their playful cubs.

FAMILY
Felidae
RANGE
Sub-Saharan Africa; one small group left in northwestern India
HABITAT
Savanna, scrubland, and tropical forest
SIZE
HB 4.6 to 6.2 feet (1.4 to 1.9 m); T 26 to 39 inches (67 to 100 cm); SH about 4 feet (1.2 m); W 330 to 551 pounds (150 to 250 kg)
LIFE CYCLE
Mating year-round; gestation 100 to 116 days, two to four cubs born

AFRICAN ELEPHANT / *Loxodonta africana*

The African elephant, the largest living land mammal, is distinguished from the smaller Indian elephant (*Elephas maximus*) by its size and huge ears, which it flaps to cool off and to keep bugs out of its eyes. The trunk, an extension of its upper lip and nose, is used for activities such as drinking, bathing, smelling, greeting, grasping, and bringing food—grasses, leaves, and fruit—to its mouth. It can eat more than three hundred pounds (135 kg) of food in a day. Cows and their calves live together in a family unit led by an older cow, the matriarch. Males are mostly solitary, meeting with females to mate. Hunted for centuries for their ivory tusks—elongated incisors—these elephants are now protected, but poaching and habitat loss still threaten them.

FAMILY
Elephantidae
RANGE
Sub-Saharan Africa, excluding southern Africa

HABITAT
Savanna in east and south; forest in west
SIZE
HB 20 to 25 feet (6 to 7.5 m); T 3.3 to 4.3 feet (1 to 1.3 m); SH 10 to 11.5 feet (3 to 3.5 m); W 8,000 to 13,000 pounds (3,600 to 5,900 kg)
LIFE CYCLE
Mating year-round; gestation about 730 days, one calf born

WHITE RHINOCEROS / *Ceratotherium simum*

The white rhinoceros, which is actually gray brown, gets its name from the Afrikaan word *weit*, meaning "wide." Ranking second among land mammals in size, it grazes on the short grasses that thrive where it lives. A solitary beast, it only comes together with other rhinos to mate. It has huge horns, measuring up to forty-eight inches (122 cm), which it uses to defend its territory, fight off predators such as lions, and dig up soil in search of mineral salts. Seriously endangered, the white rhino is now protected. Unfortunately, it continues to be poached for its horns, which are used in aphrodisiacs and folk medicine.

FAMILY
Rhinocerotidae
RANGE
South Africa, Sudan
HABITAT
Open grassland, savanna, and aridland
SIZE
HB 12 to 13 feet (3.7 to 4 m); T 15 to 28 inches (37 to 71 cm); SH 5 to 6.6 feet (1.5 to 2 m); W 5,000 to 8,000 pounds (2,300 to 3,600 kg)
LIFE CYCLE
Mating year-round, peaks February to June; gestation 470 to 490 days, one calf born

COMMON ZEBRA / *Equus burchelli*

Equus burchelli includes six subspecies that each differ in the pattern of their black and white stripes. They all graze in large herds on tall grasses. (Gnus often follow them and feed on grasses of medium height, and the gnus in turn are succeeded by gazelles, which graze on short grasses.) Some zebra herds number in the tens of thousands, but within these larger herds are distinct family groups composed of a male, several females, and their young. It has often been suggested that the stripes of zebras serve as camouflage in tall grasses. But the fact that they make no attempt to hide and freeze when a predator is seen—indeed, they become noisy and active—seems to contradict this.

FAMILY
Equidae
RANGE
East, south, southwest Africa
HABITAT
Grassland, savanna, and aridland
SIZE
HB 6.5 to 8 feet (2 to 2.5 m); T 18.5 to 22 inches (47 to 56 cm); SH 3 to 5 feet (1 to 1.5 m); W 385 to 850 pounds (175 to 385 kg)
LIFE CYCLE
Mating throughout year, peaks during wet season October to March; gestation 360 to 390, days, one foal born

ROCK HYRAX / *Procavia capensis*

Also called the rock dassie, the rock hyrax is a diurnal herbivore. Sometimes it digs its own burrow; otherwise, it shelters between and under rocks. It moves around on specialized moist, rubbery soles that improve its traction as it clambers with great agility among the rocks. The rock hyrax usually grazes on grasses and shrubs, but in some areas it climbs trees and browses on young leaves and shoots. Its food provides it with enough liquid nourishment to survive, although it will drink water if it is available. It has poor thermoregulatory abilities and so takes advantage of warm weather to bask in the hot midday sun.

FAMILY
Procaviidae
RANGE
Arabia, Middle East, and sub-Saharan Africa, except Congo basin
HABITAT
Rocky, scrubby areas in grassland and aridland

SIZE
HB 12 to 22 inches (30.5 to 55 cm); T absent; W 8 to 9 pounds (3.5 to 4 kg)
LIFE CYCLE
Mating depends on locale; gestation 202 to 245 days, usually one to three young born

AARDVARK / *Orycteropus afer*

tuber, *Cucumis humifructus*, also known as "the aardvark's cucumber." Researchers believe a symbiotic relationship exists between the two species: the tuber, which is only found in areas where aardvarks thrive, provides the aardvark with much needed water, and the aardvark disseminates the tuber's seeds in its feces.

Aardvarks, along with anteaters *(page 100)* and pangolins *(page 115)*, demonstrate convergent evolution because they have all evolved similar features—such as an elongated snout and a long sticky tongue—for feeding on ants and termites. The aardvark also possesses fur on its nostrils to exclude dust when it digs for food. It spends its days alone sleeping in burrows that are also used by other species. It also feeds on an underground

FAMILY
Orycteropodidae
RANGE
Sub-Saharan Africa
HABITAT
Primarily grassland and savanna; also woodland and tropical forest
SIZE
HB 3 to 5 feet (1 to 1.5 m); T 24 to 28 inches (60 to 70 cm); SH 22 to 26 inches (55 to 65 cm); W 110 to 176 pounds (50 to 80 kg)
LIFE CYCLE
Mating year-round, depending on locale; gestation 205 to 218 days, one (occasionally two) young born

PAMPAS DEER / *Ozotoceros bezoarticus*

All three subspecies of this medium-sized, diurnal deer were once extremely abundant and widely distributed in South America. Today, however, the populations have dropped considerably due to overhunting, habitat destruction, and disease. The deer are typically found in small groups of five to six animals in open grassy areas, where they graze on fresh green shoots and browse on trees and shrubs. Glands on the posterior hooves of the pampas deer have a distinctive garlicky odor that can be smelled over great distances.

FAMILY
Cervidae
RANGE
Brazil, south through Argentina
HABITAT
Open grasslands
SIZE
HB 3.6 to 4.6 feet (1.1 to 1.4 m); T 4 to 6 inches (10 to 15 cm); SH 28 to 30 inches (70 to 75 cm); W 55 to 88 pounds (25 to 40 kg)
LIFE CYCLE
Mating year-round; gestation 208 to 235 days, one fawn born

NILGAI / *Boselaphus tragocamelus*

The nilgai is the largest antelope native to India. Its spiraled horns and its behavior of kneeling to fight reveal its kinship to other antelopes. A herbivore, this diurnal mammal both grazes and browses for food. The females, which are brown, live in groups with their calves. The males are gray-blue, equipped with small horns eight to ten inches (20 to 25 cm) long, and have a beardlike tuft of hair on their throat. They are solitary or found in bachelor groups. Habitat loss and hunting for sport, food, and hides have led to the decline of this once abundant creature. Less than ten thousand remain alive, and it has been estimated that there are more nilgais living in captivity in zoos and on Texan game ranches than in the wild.

FAMILY
Bovidae
RANGE
India
HABITAT
Grassy regions and open woodlands
SIZE
HB 6 to 6.6 feet
(1.8 to 2 m);
T 18 to 21 inches
(46 to 54 cm);
SH 4 to 5 feet
(1.2 to 1.5 m);
W 264 to 529 pounds
(120 to 240 kg)
LIFE CYCLE
Mating usually March to April, depending on locale; gestation 210 to 250 days, one or two calves born

BLUE GNU / *Connochaetes taurinus*

The blue, or brindled, gnu is also known as the wildebeest. Like white-tailed gnus (*Connochaetes gnou*), blue gnus live in mixed herds of thirty to five hundred individuals. During the dry season, they congregate by the tens of thousands and migrate over hundreds of miles in search of water and food.

They follow zebra herds, which graze on tall grasses, leaving the shorter grasses for gnus and other herbivores. During the mating season, the males try to isolate a small harem from the larger herd to increase their chances of mating without competition. Both sexes have curved horns; males' are almost twice the size of females'.

FAMILY
Bovidae
RANGE
Southern Kenya to northern South Africa
HABITAT
Savanna and open plains
SIZE
HB 6 to 8 feet (1.8 to 2.4 m);
T 24 to 39 inches (60 to 100 cm); SH 3 to 4.3 feet (1 to 1.3 m); W 500 to 600 pounds (230 to 275 kg)
LIFE CYCLE
Mating in May; gestation 240 to 260 days, one calf born

BLACKBUCK / *Antilope cervicapra*

In most antelope species, all members are similarly colored, but in *Antilope cervicapra* the dominant male is black and white, while the female *(right)* and young are light brown and white. Males are also distinguished by their twisted spiraling horns, which measure up to twenty-four inches (60 cm). Herds of blackbucks may number up to fifty individuals. As young males mature, they are pushed out of the herd by the dominant male. Today blackbucks are rare outside of game reserves and parks, where they can sometimes be seen grazing in the early morning and late afternoon.

FAMILY
Bovidae
RANGE
Pakistan, India, Nepal

HABITAT
Grassy plains to dry woodlands
SIZE
HB 3 to 5 feet (1 to 1.5 m); T 4 to 7 inches (10 to 17 cm); SH 24 to 33 inches (60 to 85 cm); W 55 to 88 pounds (25 to 40 kg)
LIFE CYCLE
Mating February to March; gestation 160 to 180 days, one or two young born

THOMSON'S GAZELLE / *Gazella thomsoni*

Thomson's gazelles are mainly grazers, feeding on grasses, herbs, and leaves of plants in the open plains. Their herds, which are composed of a dominant male, females, and their young, contain anywhere from five to fifty individuals. The dominant male marks off his territory with urine and feces and regularly patrols its perimeter to keep his herd together. When he meets another male, they go head to head and push each other to establish rank. Thomson's gazelles are known for a behavior called stotting: They bounce on all fours in a stiff-legged fashion that propels them up into the air, providing them with a better view of approaching danger and making them less vulnerable to attack.

FAMILY
Bovidae
RANGE
Kenya, Tanzania, southern Sudan
HABITAT
Grassy plains to brushy forests
SIZE
HB 31 to 43 inches (80 to 110 cm); T 7.5 to 11 inches (19 to 27 cm); SH 22 to 26 inches (55 to 65 cm); W 33 to 66 pounds (15 to 30 kg)
LIFE CYCLE
Mating January to February and in July; gestation 160 to 180 days, one (rarely two) calves born; sometimes two births per year

GIRAFFE / *Giraffa camelopardalis*

Giraffes are the tallest land mammals in the world, with heads that may tower twenty feet (6 m) above ground. Their great height allows them to reach the leaves of the spiny trees that are their staple.

They pluck the buds, fruit, and leaves of these trees with prehensile upper lips and long tongues that can be extended up to eighteen inches (45 cm). They also eat grasses, seeds, grains, and other low-lying vegetation. Their herds of twenty to forty individuals are led by a dominant, usually old, bull. Shy animals, they possess keen senses of smell and hearing, which help them stay clear of predators. Once widespread and abundant, giraffes have been heavily hunted for their flesh and their hide.

FAMILY
Giraffidae
RANGE
Sub-Saharan Africa
HABITAT
Savanna to open woodland
SIZE
HB 12.5 to 15.5 feet (3.8 to 4.7 m); T 31 to 41 inches (79 to 104 cm); SH 8 to 12 feet (2.5 to 3.7 m); W 1,200 to 4,250 pounds (550 to 1,930 kg)
LIFE CYCLE
Mating depends on locale; gestation 400 to 460 days, one (rarely two) young born

CAVY / *Cavia apera*

Cavies, also known as guinea pigs, are most active in the early evening and into the night, when they forage for grass, seeds, fruit, flowers, and leaves. They travel along paths through the grass and take shelter from predators in dense vegetation. They live in small groups, or colonies, with a distinct dominance hierarchy,

yet they do not define individual territories. It is believed that the domestic guinea pig may have been derived from this species. During the Inca empire (A.D. 1200 to 1532), Cavies were selectively bred to produce differently colored and flavored varieties. To this day they are kept for food by people in northern South America.

FAMILY
Caviidae
RANGE
Colombia to southern Argentina
HABITAT
Moist grassland
SIZE
HB 8 to 12 inches (20 to 30 cm); T absent; W about 1 pound (0.5 kg)
LIFE CYCLE
Mating year-round when conditions favorable; gestation about 60 days, one to four young born; up to five litters per year

Aridland

Extreme temperatures and low rainfall typify the aridlands of the world *(map, pages 84 to 85)*. These regions range from the semi-arid scrub forests of the Middle East, which receive an annual rainfall of ten to twelve inches (25 to 30 cm), to the Asian Gobi Desert, where the driest areas receive less than three inches (8 cm) of rain per year. In between lie regions known as Mediterranean, where summer drought places heavy demands on the plant and animal species that live there.

Survival for most aridland plant life depends on an array of structures that gather and retain moisture, including extensive root systems, shiny succulent leaves that hold moisture, and even, in the case of the *welwitschia* of the Namib Desert, leaves with the ability to absorb humidity from nighttime mist.

Mammals, too, are ingeniously adapted to withstand the difficult conditions. The camel, for example, uses its hump to store fat, which, during prolonged dry periods, is metabolized to produce water. The body temperature of the camel and another large aridland mammal, the gemsbok *(page 138)*, fluctuates rapidly in response to external temperature changes, allowing them to expend less energy staying warm when temperatures drop at night. Equally important, water is not wasted in cooling the body during the scorching heat of day.

Many small aridland mammals are nocturnal, responding to the heat by spending the day burrowed in soil or sand. Some, such as the lesser Egyptian jerboa *(page 139)*, the African jird, and the Ord's kangaroo rat *(page 140)*, have developed common physical traits to cope, showing convergent evolution at work. These rodents all have enlarged hindlegs and long tails to help them hop on shifting sands.

California's Death Valley is the lowest, hottest, and driest portion of the North American continent. Yet it hosts a rich variety of aridland wildlife—including kangaroo rats, ground squirrels, bats, coyotes, bighorn sheep, mountain lions, and bobcats. Primarily nocturnal, these mammals are rarely seen by visitors to the valley.

SHORT-NOSED ECHIDNA / *Tachyglossus aculeatus*

The short-nosed echidna is one of two echidnas (both known as spiny anteaters) in the family Tachyglossidae that—along with the duck-billed platypus *(page 97)*—make up the monotremes *(page 15)*. It is toothless and has a long sticky tongue for lapping up ants and termites. Mixed in with the hair on its back are hard quills; its stomach is covered in fur. The quills appear

about fifty-five days after hatching, at which point the infant is no longer carried in the pouch but left in a sheltered place. For the next three months, the mother returns regularly to nurse it, but instead of nipples, she has—like the platypus—specialized areas of skin that exude milk. When threatened, this nocturnal creature burrows into the ground or rolls up into a ball.

FAMILY
Tachyglossidae
RANGE
Australia, New Guinea, Tasmania
HABITAT
Arid regions, including grasslands, forests, and rocky areas
SIZE
HB 12 to 18 inches (30 to 45 cm); T 3 to 3.5 inches (7 to 9 cm); W 5.5 to 13 pounds (2.5 to 6 kg)
LIFE CYCLE
Mating July to August; usually one egg laid, incubated 9 to 27 days; young stays in mother's pouch until quills grow

KULTARR / *Antechinomys laniger*

The kultarr is a nocturnal terrestrial marsupial that shelters during the day in the burrows of other mammals, under debris, or in cracks in the ground. At night it forages for small vertebrates and insects, such as crickets and cockroaches. It is endowed with long granular pads on its hind feet for traction and elongated fore limbs to help

it pivot and change direction in mid-gallop. During the breeding season, the front-opening pouch becomes enlarged from side to side and partially covers the nipples. After about thirty days in the pouch, the mother places the young in a sheltered nest or carries them around on her back. She continues to nurse them until they are about three months old.

FAMILY
Dasyuridae
RANGE
Australia
HABITAT
Sparsely vegetative arid areas
SIZE
HB 3 to 4 inches (8 to 11 cm); T 4 to 6 inches (10 to 14.5 cm); W 0.7 to 1.2 ounces (20 to 35 g)
LIFE CYCLE
Mating June to January; gestation about 12 days; six to eight young born that stay in mother's pouch about 30 days

GREATER BILBY / *Macrotis lagotis*

The greater bilby is also called the rabbit bandicoot. It is a burrowing marsupial with a hopping gait similar to that of a rabbit. It builds burrows to a depth of about six feet (2 m), where it rests during the day when temperatures soar. When it sleeps, it squats on its rear legs, using its tail for balance, tucks its head between its legs, and covers its eyes with its long ears. At night the greater bilby comes out to forage for ants, termites, beetles, insect larvae, seeds, fruit, and some herbs. Typically solitary, it sometimes forms colonies. Although once distributed over most of southern Australia, populations are now sparse due to habitat loss, predation by exotic species, the fur trade, and ranching.

FAMILY
Thylacomydae
RANGE
Northern Territory, Queensland, and western Australia

HABITAT
Arid regions
SIZE
HB 8 to 22 inches (20 to 55 cm); T 4.5 to 11 inches (11.5 to 27.5 cm); W 0.7 to 3.5 pounds (0.3 to 1.6 kg)
LIFE CYCLE
Mating March to May; gestation about 14 days, one to three young born that stay in mother's pouch about 75 days

BRUSH-TAILED RAT KANGAROO / *Bettongia penicillata*

Also called the woylie or brush-tailed bettong, the brush-tailed rat kangaroo once enjoyed a wide range in western and southeastern Australia. Today only four populations remain, surviving on reserves and in state forests located at the southwestern tip of the continent. A nocturnal marsupial, it shelters during the day in a grass nest and comes out at night to forage on seeds, roots, tubers, mushrooms, and occasional-

ly insects. Although it resembles a rat, it has strong hind limbs and long feet like a kangaroo. When it runs, it holds its head low with its back arched and its brushy tail displayed.

FAMILY
Macropodidae
RANGE
Remnant populations in southwestern Australia

HABITAT
Semi-arid regions from scrubland and grassland to forest and woodland
SIZE
HB 11 to 16 inches (28 to 41 cm); T 8 to 9 inches (20 to 25 cm); W 2.4 to 3.5 pounds (1.1 to 1.6 kg)
LIFE CYCLE
Mating throughout year; gestation about 21 days, usually one young born that stays in mother's pouch 90 to 115 days

QUOKKA / *Setonix brachyurus*

In southwestern Australia, the quokka generally comes out only at night to feed on vegetation, but on the islands off the coast, it is often seen during the day. After the first young is born, it moves to the pouch and the female immediately becomes fertile and mates again. The resulting embryo is implanted in the uterus, but development is delayed until the first young leaves the pouch—about 175 to 195 days later—at which time the process may be repeated. During peri-

ods of drought, the quokka scavenges for food in garbage dumps and will travel long distances in search of water. Also, the male may become very aggressive and fight with other quokkas over shady areas. Much of the animal's habitat has been destroyed by soil erosion caused by over-grazing of cattle and the subsequent invasion of exotic plants, which compete with indigenous plants that make up the bulk of the quokka diet.

FAMILY
Macropodidae
RANGE
Southwestern Australia and some surrounding islands
HABITAT
Shrubby coastal areas and sometimes swamp valleys
SIZE
HB 19 to 24 inches (47.5 to 60 cm); T 10 to 14 inches (25 to 35 cm); W 4 to 11 pounds (2 to 5 kg)
LIFE CYCLE
Mating throughout year; gestation 26 to 28 days, one young born

PINK FAIRY ARMADILLO / *Chlamyphorus truncatus*

Little is known about the rare and endangered pink fairy armadillo. Smallest of the armadillos, this nocturnal creature is sometimes called the lesser fairy armadillo because it is smaller than the greater fairy armadillo (*Chlamyphorus retusus*). It gets its name from the pink-colored shield that covers its head, back, and rump. In Spanish it was once known as *Juan calado*, or "lacy Jack," in reference to the fringe of white hair found at the rear of its armored plate. Equipped with heavy claws for excavating tunnels, it lives primarily underground, hardly ever coming to the surface. It feeds on seeds and subterranean creatures such as worms, ants, and their larvae.

FAMILY
Dasypodidae
RANGE
Central and western Argentina

HABITAT
Sandy dry areas with thorny vegetation
SIZE
HB 4 to 6 inches (11 to 15 cm); T 1 to 1.4 inches (2.5 to 3.5 cm); W about 3.5 ounces (100 g)
LIFE CYCLE
Little is known

BRANDT'S HEDGEHOG / *Hemiechinus hypomelas*

Unlike other hedgehogs, this terrestrial mammal is not an active burrower. It tends to be nomadic, moving from place to place during the day to forage for small vertebrates and insects, as well as fruit and plants. Its body is covered with thousands of prickly spines, and when threatened it rolls into a ball. Before birth the young is covered with only a fraction of the spines found on an adult, and its skin swells to cover the spines during parturition.

FAMILY
Erinaceidae
RANGE
Arabia
HABITAT
Desert and arid regions

SIZE
HB 5.5 to 11 inches (14 to 27 cm); T 0.5 to 1.5 inches (1 to 4 cm); W 1 to 1.5 pounds (0.4 to 0.7 kg)
LIFE CYCLE
Little is known; gestation 35 to 39 days in captivity, three or four young born

SPOTTED BAT / *Euderma maculatum*

Sometimes called the death's-head bat because of the ghostly pattern of white patches on its shoulders, the spotted bat is rare. It has been found roosting in rocky pockets along cliffs and canyon walls and hibernating in small clusters. Unlike that of many other bat species, its echolocation call is a high-pitched cry within the range of human hearing. Foraging forays occur late at night, when the bat may prey on moths, eating the juicy bits and discarding the exoskeleton and wings.

FAMILY
Vespertilionidae
RANGE
Southwestern Canada through western United States into Mexico
HABITAT
Desert, scrubland, coniferous forest, dry woodland
SIZE
HB about 2.5 inches (6.5 cm); T about 2 inches (5 cm); FA about 2 inches (5 cm); W 0.4 to 0.7 ounce (10 to 20 g)

LIFE CYCLE
Little is known; gestation possibly about 40 days, one young born June to August

RHESUS MACAQUE / *Macaca mulatta*

Highly adaptable, rhesus macaques can be found in a variety of habitats and are unusual in that they have long been associated with humans in settled areas. Many are exported to laboratories around the world and used in medical research. Wild rhesus macaques forage for fruit, sprouts, leaves, berries, and insects. They may either be solitary or belong to social groups of up to thirty-five or more individuals that are led by a founding female. The groups often have overlapping ranges, and when water is scarce they may form aggregations of up to two hundred while sharing a single watering hole. When a group becomes too large, it splits to form two separate groups. The groups live both on the ground and in trees, where they usually sleep.

FAMILY
Cercopithecidae
RANGE
Asia, especially Afghanistan, India, China, Myanmar, northern Thailand
HABITAT
Arid regions, woodlands, forests
SIZE
HB 14 to 20 inches (35 to 50 cm); T 8 to 10 inches (20 to 25 cm); W 13 to 22 pounds (6 to 10 kg)
LIFE CYCLE
Mating September to October, gestation 135 to 194 days, one young born

FENNEC FOX / *Vulpes zerda*

The fennec fox, smallest of all canids, is well adapted to desert life: Its body is small; its hair is light-colored to reduce heat absorption; and its large ears are highly vascularized to facilitate cooling. Also, its feet have hairy soles for traction and heat protection in sand, and it can sustain long periods without drinking. These foxes dig multi- chambered dens in the sand and rest there during the day, shielded from the sun. At night they venture forth to hunt insects and small vertebrates. Once they locate their prey, they dig in the sand at high speed to catch it. Fennec foxes live in groups of ten to fifteen individuals and mated pairs are believed to bond for life.

FAMILY
Canidae
RANGE
Northern Africa, Sahara, Arabia
HABITAT
Deserts and areas of sand dunes
SIZE
HB 15 to 16 inches (37 to 41 cm); T 7.5 to 8 inches (19 to 21 cm); W 2 to 3 pounds (1 to 1.5 kg)
LIFE CYCLE
Little is known; mating in captivity January to February; gestation about 50 days, two to five cubs born

KIT FOX / *Vulpes velox*

The color of the kit fox, also known as the swift fox, varies according to region. Nocturnal carnivores, kit foxes prey on rodents, rabbits, hares, and sometimes ground-nesting birds and reptiles. During the day, they shelter in burrows, which may have up to twenty-four entrances. Each burrow is typically occupied by a single fox. Cubs are born blind and helpless, and the mother rarely leaves the den while nursing. During this time, the male hunts and provides food and nourishment for the nursing female. At about one month, the cubs are sufficiently developed to venture outside to romp, play, and begin learning to hunt for themselves.

FAMILY
Canidae
RANGE
Southwestern Canada and western United States into north central Mexico
HABITAT
Prairie and semi-arid regions
SIZE
HB 15 to 20 inches (37.5 to 50 cm); T 8 to 13 inches (22.5 to 32.5 cm); SH 10 to 12 inches (25 to 30 cm); W 3 to 7 pounds (1.5 to 3 kg)
LIFE CYCLE
Mating December to February; gestation 49 to 56 days, four or five cubs born

MEERKAT / *Suricata suricatta*

The meerkat, also called the slender-tailed meerkat or suricate, is the only species in its genus *Suricata*. A small mongoose, it lives in large social colonies made up of several family units. It is often found in association with other mongoose species, as well as squirrels and various other rodents. It has many chatterlike calls in its repertoire. During the night, it shelters in a multi-chambered burrow; in the daytime, it basks in the sun near the entrance or goes foraging for insects, small mammals, reptiles, birds, birds' eggs, fruit, and vegetation. It has highly developed senses of smell, vision, and hearing, and may sometimes be seen standing up on its hindlegs, alert to danger.

When a meerkat spots a predator, it will sound an alarm call to warn the others of the colony.

FAMILY
Viverridae
RANGE
Southern Africa
HABITAT
Savanna and arid open plains
SIZE
HB 10 to 14 inches (25 to 35 cm); T 7.5 to 9 inches (19 to 24 cm); W 1.3 to 2.2 pounds (0.6 to 1 kg)
LIFE CYCLE
Mating usually September to October; gestation about 77 days, two to five young born

ASIAN WILD ASS / *Equus hemionus*

The Asian wild ass, also called the onager, is endangered because of overhunting, loss of habitat, and competition with livestock for grazing land. Today it lives in small groups led by a male or a mature female, but at one time herds of fifty to one hundred individuals were sighted following rainy periods. Asian wild asses eat mostly grasses and will travel long distances to winter feeding grounds or to seek out a watering hole that will get them through a dry summer. They can run faster than any other horse or ass, reaching and sustaining speeds of up to about forty-four miles (70 km) per hour. There are four subspecies, each associated with a particular area. A fifth subspecies, which once ranged from Palestine to Iraq, is now extinct.

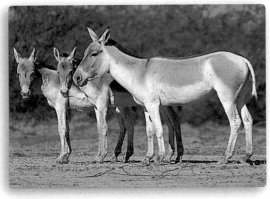

FAMILY
Equidae
RANGE
Central Asia
HABITAT
Steppe and desert
SIZE
HB 6.5 to 8 feet (2 to 2.5 m);
T 12 to 16 inches (30 to 40 cm);
SH 3 to 5 feet (1 to 1.4 m); W 440
to 570 pounds (200 to 260 kg)
LIFE CYCLE
Mating April to October, varying by locale; gestation about 330 days, one foal born

KIRK'S DIKDIK / *Madoqua kirkii*

This small desert antelope has a flexible snout, or proboscis, lined with numerous blood vessels that serves as a heat exchanger. Cooled blood then passes directly to the brain, protecting this vital organ from increased body temperature in the heat of the day. The dikdik may be active by day or night and is usually about when the moon is full. It eats shoots and leaves of shrubs and succulents. Family groups, consisting of an adult pair and their young, live in well-defined territories that they protect from neighboring families. Dung, urine, and secretions from facial glands are used to mark territorial boundaries and are deposited by each family member. They will also add their own dung to

any strong-smelling substance they encounter in their territory. The male dikdik whistles to warn of danger; different whistles elicit different responses from the female and young: They may run and hide or join together to mob a predator.

FAMILY
Bovidae
RANGE
Isolated populations in east and southwest Africa
HABITAT
Arid areas with thickets and shrubs on stony soil
SIZE
HB 22 to 28 inches (55 to 70 cm); T 1.6 to 2.4 inches (4 to 6 cm); W 9 to 15 pounds (4 to 7 kg)
LIFE CYCLE
Gestation about 180 days, one young born; two births per year

AOUDAD / *Ammotragus lervia*

This species is also known as the Barbary sheep. It lives in family units led by a dominant female. The groups wander from place to place, foraging on grass, herbs, leaves, and twigs. Like goats, the aoudad is able to rise on its hindlegs to reach the foliage of dwarf acacias. It is able to obtain most of its water from the plants it eats and by licking the dew off vegetation. When its predators, the desert lynx and the leopard, were common in its habitat, it could escape them by leaping and bounding across the rocky terrain.

FAMILY
Bovidae
RANGE
Isolated populations in northern Africa; introduced and established in United States
HABITAT
Dry, rocky, barren regions of montane Sahara
SIZE
HB 4.3 to 6 feet (1.3 to 1.9 m); T 6 to 10 inches (15 to 25 cm); SH 29.5 to 44 inches (75 to 112 cm); W 88 to 320 pounds (40 to 145 kg)

LIFE CYCLE
Mating year-round, peaks vary by region; gestation 154 to 161 days, one or two young born

EDMI / *Gazella gazella*

The edmi, also known as the mountain gazelle, lives in mixed-sex herds of up to forty individuals that roam their arid habitat eating almost anything green. In mid-winter, the males establish territories that they defend from rivals. The male is generally larger than the female *(right)* and has S-shaped horns more than twice as big. Hunted for sport, the population of edmi is now greatly diminished and its range is fragmented.

FAMILY
Bovidae
RANGE
Arabian peninsula
HABITAT
Sandy and stony hills, steppe, and montane desert
SIZE
HB 37 to 41 inches (95 to 105 cm); T 6 to 8 inches (15 to 20 cm); SH 24 to 31 inches (60 to 80 cm); W 33 to 77 pounds (15 to 35 kg)
LIFE CYCLE
Mating throughout year if water available, peaks December to January; gestation 175 to 190 days, one young born

GOITERED GAZELLE / *Gazella subgutturosa*

The goitered gazelle is so named because the neck of the male swells during the mating season to form a goiter. These gazelles live much of the year in groups of six to twelve individuals. They feed mainly at night, taking advantage of the cooler temperatures, and are able to obtain most of their moisture from the grasses, herbs, and buds they eat. Mating occurs in the wintertime, when the small groups migrate, joining up with others to form a large aggregation for winter feeding. Adult males mark twigs with their facial glands and leave dung piles to establish territories. The mating ritual is similar to the patterns of other gazelles: The male follows the female with his head and neck extended. He then kicks with his forelegs before walking on hindlegs and mounting her.

FAMILY
Bovidae
RANGE
Arabia to central Asia
HABITAT
Desert and desert steppe
SIZE
HB 35 to 45 inches (90 to 115 cm);
T 6 to 8 inches (15 to 20 cm);
SH 24 to 31 inches (60 to 80 cm);
W 40 to 73 pounds (18 to 33 kg)
LIFE CYCLE
Mating November to January; gestation 150 to 180 days, usually one or two young born

GEMSBOCK / *Oryx gazella*

Herds of ten to forty gemsbock are not uncommon and groups of up to a hundred have been recorded. These animals are frequently found in association with other species of gazelles and sometimes zebras, foraging for grasses and leaves. Gemsbock can go many days without water, but in the more arid parts of their range, they sometimes dig a trough in a dried-out river bed to reach the water table below and quench their thirst. The males are often found alone and may be quite aggressive. When they fight, they lower their heads and fence, their long horns pointing straight out. These "sword fights" are for display and rarely shed blood.

FAMILY
Bovidae
RANGE
From Ethiopia and Somalia to Namibia and eastern South Africa
HABITAT
Arid regions and savannas
SIZE
HB 6 to 8 feet (1.8 to 2.4 m); T 31 to 35 inches (80 to 90 cm); SH 4 to 4.5 feet (1.2 to 1.4 m); W 400 to 500 pounds (180 to 225 kg)
LIFE CYCLE
Gestation 260 to 300 days, one young born

GUANACO / *Lama guanicoe*

Guanacos are usually found in small herds or loosely structured family groups. When a member of the herd picks up the slightest hint of danger, it makes a high-pitched warning call, causing the other guanacos to flee swiftly and nimbly across the steep and uneven terrain. Guanacos generally live at high elevations, grazing on grasses and browsing on leaves and buds. They can get by without water for long periods of time, obtaining moisture from the plants they eat. The young play and romp, but when confronted by an adult male they will lay their neck on the ground in submission. The guanaco is one of the largest wild mammals in South America, and the puma is its only significant natural predator. Classified as endangered in Chile and Peru, its numbers in Chile appear to be increasing.

FAMILY
Camelidae
RANGE
Andes from Peru to Patagonia
HABITAT
Arid montane regions and grasslands
SIZE
HB 5 to 6.5 feet (1.5 to 2 m);
T 9 to 10 inches (22 to 25 cm);
SH 35 to 47 inches (90 to 120 cm); W 176 to 265 pounds (80 to 120 kg)
LIFE CYCLE
Mating November to February; gestation 300 to 330 days, one calf born

DESERT WARTHOG / *Phacochoerus aethiopicus*

Wartlike growths up to six inches (15 cm) long on the eyes and under the jaws are responsible for the name of this species. These protuberances are thought to protect against injuries that might otherwise occur when desert warthogs fight. Small family groups of six to eighteen females plus their offspring are common. The males are usually solitary, but may form bachelor groups. Occasionally several small groups come together to form a clan. Diurnal vegetarians, they feed on grasses and seeds, as well as roots, tubers, and bulbs. They allow birds called oxpeckers to alight on their back and pick off parasites. Wallowing in mud also helps get rid of the parasites while simultaneously providing relief from the heat of the day.

FAMILY
Suidae
RANGE
Sub-Saharan Africa
HABITAT
Arid grassland, savanna, and open plains

SIZE
HB 3.6 to 4.6 feet (1.1 to 1.4 m);
T 14 to 20 inches (35 to 50 cm);
SH 25 to 29.5 inches (64 to 75 cm);
W 106 to 315 pounds (48 to 143 kg)
LIFE CYCLE
Mating associated with rainy season; gestation 170 to 175 days, usually two to four young born

LESSER EGYPTIAN JERBOA / *Jaculus jaculus*

The lesser Egyptian jerboa is the smallest species in its genus *Jaculus*. It lives a solitary nocturnal life, feeding on roots, sprouts, seeds, grains, and vegetable crops and sheltering in its burrow, especially during extreme heat. A tunnel leads from the burrow entrance to a vegetation-lined chamber where the animal dwells; the burrow has at least one or two exits near the surface for quick escape. Kangaroo-like adaptations such as long hind feet relative to body length allow the lesser Egyptian jerboa to jump nearly ten times its own body length. Another desert adaptation is its hair-fringed toes, which provide traction and prevent it from sinking in the sand.

FAMILY
Dipodidae
RANGE
Northern Africa and Arabia
HABITAT
Desert to semi-desert

SIZE
HB 4 to 5 inches (9.5 to 12 cm); T 6 to 8 inches (16 to 20 cm); W 1.4 to 2.5 ounces (40 to 70 g)
LIFE CYCLE
Breeding may vary with climate and resource availability; gestation 22 to 25 days, three or four young born

PATAGONIAN CAVY / *Dolichotis patagonum*

The Patagonian cavy, also called the Patagonian hare, has long legs similar to those of rabbits and hares. In areas without lagomorphs, it may fill the same niche; where the European hare *(page 159)* has been introduced, its numbers are in decline. When chased, the Patagonian cavy can gallop at fifty miles (80 km) per hour, making leaps of six feet (2 m). Groups of as many as forty may come together to feed on grasses, acacia seeds, and sometimes cactus. Within these groups, pairs and occasionally trios bond, staying together year-round. The young of twenty or so pairs stay in communal burrows; the mothers visit the burrows regularly, whistling to the young to come out and nurse.

FAMILY
Caviidae
RANGE
Patagonia, central and southern Argentina
HABITAT
Open arid grassland

SIZE
HB 27 to 29.5 inches (69 to 75 cm); T about 2 inches (4 cm); W 20 to 33 pounds (9 to 15 kg)
LIFE CYCLE
Little is known; mating year-round in captivity; gestation 80 to 90 days, two to five young born

ORD'S KANGAROO RAT / *Dipodomys ordii*

This kangaroo rat, named after the American zoologist George Ord, acquires most of the water it needs from the seeds, grasses, and herbs that it eats. To conserve moisture, it remains in its shallow, multichambered burrow during the day and is equipped with specialized kidneys that require less water to process waste. It possesses strong hindlegs for leaping and a tail for balance and support. Endowed with excellent

hearing, it can sense the imminent strike of a rattlesnake or attack of an owl or a bat and leap out of the way in time. It has also been observed kicking sand in a predator's face before it runs away and hides. When threatened, it beats its feet against the ground, making a drumming sound to warn others of the danger.

FAMILY
Heteromyidae
RANGE
From south central Canada
to central Mexico
HABITAT
Open sandy areas with sparse vegetation
SIZE
HB 4.3 to 4.7 inches (11 to 12 cm);
T 4 to 6 inches (10 to 16 cm);
W 1.8 to 3.5 ounces (50 to 100 g)
LIFE CYCLE
Mating associated with seasonal rains; gestation about 30 days, three to five young born

CACTUS MOUSE / *Peromyscus eremicus*

The cactus mouse is usually found in desert outcroppings where cactus and yucca plants grow. It builds nests in clumps of prickly cactus plants, which offer some degree of protection against predators. This little mouse is well adapted to its desert environment; it can tolerate soaring temperatures and needs little water compared to its

deer-mice relatives. During the day, it shelters from the heat in burrows that it builds or that have been constructed by other rodents. At night it comes out to feed on the fruit and flowers of mesquite and hackberry, as well as the seeds from various perennial plants. It can store large quantities of food and survive extended periods of drought by going into a state of torpor *(page 11)*.

FAMILY
Muridae
RANGE
Southwestern United States
into Mexico
HABITAT
Desert to semi-desert
SIZE
HB 3 to 3.5 inches (8 to 9 cm);
T 4 to 5.5 inches (10 to 14 cm);
W 0.7 to 1.4 ounces (20 to 40 g)
LIFE CYCLE
Mating year-round; gestation about
21 days, two or three young born

NAKED MOLE-RAT / *Heterocephalus glaber*

The naked mole-rat is the only member of its genus *Heterocephalus*. Except for a few vibrissae and pale colored hairs, its wrinkled body is entirely hairless. It lives in underground colonies made up of twenty to one hundred individuals and it is considered to be eusocial—highly social and interdependent in the way of ants and bees. Only one female in the colony, the queen, reproduces; researchers believe that she is somehow able to suppress the ovulation of the other females. Worker mole-rats provide food and nest material and maintain the tunnel system, while another group is often found in close association with the queen, but their function is unknown. Naked mole-rats are completely subterranean and their tunnel systems help to aerate the soil. They forage on the underground portions of plants such as tubers and roots.

FAMILY
Bathyergidae
RANGE
Eastern Africa
HABITAT
Arid regions
SIZE
HB 3 to 3.5 inches (8 to 9 cm); T 1.2 to 1.6 inches (3 to 4 cm); W 1 to 3 ounces (30 to 80 g)
LIFE CYCLE
Mating throughout year; gestation 66 to 74 days, three to twelve young born

CRESTED PORCUPINE / *Hystrix indica*

There are three species in the genus *Hystrix*, including *H. indica*, which derives its common name, crested porcupine, from its ability to form a crest by erecting the quills on the head, back, and nape. It also possesses specialized rattle quills on its tail that it can agitate, making a startling whizzing sound that sometimes deters predators. When that doesn't work, the porcupine turns around and rams the predator with its quills. It shares its burrow with a family group composed of up to fifteen other individuals. They forage primarily on fallen fruits, roots, tubers, and seasonal bulbs. They also gnaw on bones, sharpening their teeth and perhaps acquiring supplementary calcium for their diet.

FAMILY
Hystricidae
RANGE
Southwestern and south central Asia

HABITAT
Dry rocky areas
SIZE
HB 24 to 35 inches (60 to 90 cm); T 3 to 7 inches (8 to 7 cm); W 22 to 66 pounds (10 to 30 kg)
LIFE CYCLE
Mating throughout year, depending on locale; gestation about 60 days, one or two young born

Temperate Grassland

Today about a quarter of the Earth's surface that supports vegetation is made up of temperate grassland *(map, pages 84 to 85)*. While a large portion of this land was once forest and has been degraded to grass by human development, many original temperate grasslands still exist.

Perhaps the harshest of all grassland biomes are those of the Eurasian steppes and northwestern North America. Even so, despite the low winter temperatures, a rich summer growth of vegetation supports a variety of mammal species here, including ungulates—such as the saiga antelope *(page 145)* and the pronghorn *(page 146)*—that

share a common ancestry with the antelopes and gazelles of Africa.

Many rodent species on the grasslands survive winter by tunneling into the soft, dry soil, where they hibernate and store food. Susliks and marmots in Eurasia and prairie dogs in North America make up a large percentage of these species and, in turn, support predators, including the coyote *(page opposite)*, which is widely distributed in North America, and the gray wolf *(page 163)*, which is also distributed in Eurasia.

Mammals of the pampas grasslands of South America show some striking similarities to those found in grasslands of the northern hemisphere. The niches of the prairie dogs and coyotes, for instance, are here represented by the viscacha (*Lagostomus maximus*), another burrowing rodent, and the maned wolf (*Chrysocyon brachyurus*). Only distantly related to true wolves, this South American canid has unusually long legs, permitting it to bound above tall grass in search of prey.

Temperature extremes and a lack of natural shelter have conditioned the mammals that can inhabit the eastern steppe—burrowing rodents such as marmots and mice, as well as fox, wolf, and skunk.

COYOTE / *Canis latrans*

The term "wily coyote" was possibly coined in response to this intelligent canid's problem-solving abilities when hunting prey. Coyotes will not only wade in the water to catch fish and forage along the banks for crayfish or turtle eggs, but they will also ambush a ground squirrel by waiting at one of the burrow's exits as a badger digs its way in at the entrance or, when hunting in pairs, distract the attention of the prey while the other coyote sneaks up from behind. In general, they eat a variety of food items, including small rodents, rabbits, and carrion, as well as some fruits and plants. They do not, however, prey on large game.

FAMILY
Canidae
RANGE
Central America to Alaska
HABITAT
Open areas in forests or at forest edges
SIZE
HB 3.3 to 4.6 feet (1 to 1.4 m); T 11 to 12 inches (28 to 30 cm); W 33 to 44 pounds (15 to 20 kg)
LIFE CYCLE
Mating January to March; gestation 60 to 64 days, five to ten young born

BLACK-FOOTED FERRET / *Mustela nigripes*

This little-known species lives in the tunnels of the black-tailed prairie dog *(page 148)* and feeds on them as well as other small mammals and ground-nesting birds. It tends to hunt at night, killing its prey with a single bite at the base of the skull. Its own predators are primarily owls and other predatory birds. Since its favorite prey, the black-tailed prairie dog, has been exterminated in many areas, the once-common black-footed ferret has become extremely rare; it was considered extinct in the wild by 1987 and has since been reintroduced in several areas.

FAMILY
Mustelidae
RANGE
Southwestern Canada to Arizona, Oklahoma, and northwestern Texas
HABITAT
Prairie
SIZE
HB 15 to 18 inches (38 to 45 cm); T 5 to 6 inches (12.5 to 15 cm); W about 1 pound (0.5 kg)
LIFE CYCLE
Mating in spring; gestation 42 to 45 days, three to five young born

STEPPE POLECAT / *Mustela eversmanni*

The steppe polecat is a member of the weasel family. Extremely agile and endowed with well-developed senses of hearing and smell, it is a skillful hunter, catching as much as one-third its body weight in food in a twenty-four-hour period. Steppe polecats often live within the confines of a suslik (*Spermophillus citellus*) colony, a main dietary staple, or in burrows of other mammals, which they modify, adding intricate tunnel systems. They sometimes store dead prey, which includes other small rodents, hares, and birds. Western Siberian populations contain large individuals called "grave diggers"—so-named because they are erroneously believed to rob graves in cemeteries, places where they often live.

FAMILY
Mustelidae
RANGE
Eurasia

HABITAT
Steppe and arid regions
SIZE
HB 11 to 22 inches (29 to 56 cm); T 3 to 7 inches (7 to 18 cm); W 2 to 4 pounds (1 to 2 kg)
LIFE CYCLE
Mating February to March; gestation 36 to 42 days, usually three to six (may be up to eighteen) young born

VICUÑA / *Vicugna vicugna*

Vicuñas are the smallest members of the camel family, Camelidae. These social animals live in family groups of up to twenty-five individuals, which usually consist of one dominant male and his harem of females and their young. The male is extremely protective of his harem. He has a specialized call to warn of potential predators and he fights with other males—bouts in which, among other things, the opponents may spit at each other. Vicuñas descend from the hills during the day to feed on grasses and other vegetation, then return to the hills to sleep. They are now rare, having been heavily exploited to obtain their coat, which is said to make the best wool in the world. Despite legal protection and the establishment of captive populations, they are still being poached from the few reserves where they survive.

FAMILY
Camelidae
RANGE
Central Andes
HABITAT
Semi-arid grassland in montane regions
SIZE
HB 4 to 6 feet (1.2 to 1.8 m); T 5 to 6 inches (12 to 15 cm); SH 30 to 39 inches (75 to 100 cm); W 88 to 132 pounds (40 to 60 kg)
LIFE CYCLE
Mating March to April; gestation 330 to 350 days, one young born

SAIGA ANTELOPE / *Saiga tatarica*

The saiga is distinguished by its soft, oddly shaped nose. Otherwise it resembles a thin-legged sheep. This has resulted in confusion over how to classify it. It has been lumped with goats, gazelles, and antelopes, but is now recognized as an intermediate species between sheep and antelopes. It lives in herds of thirty to forty individuals, and during the mating season the males form harems of five to fifteen females. The species is constantly roaming and some populations make long migrations, usually triggered by extreme conditions such as drought or severe storms. During a ten-year period in the 1800s, when its numbers were reduced by overhunting to about a thousand, a single harsh winter would have wiped it out. Fortunately, protective measures and managed hunting have brought a rebound in its numbers.

FAMILY
Bovidae
RANGE
Central western Asia
HABITAT
Saline, muddy steppe
SIZE
HB 37 to 53 inches (95 to 135 cm); T 2 to 5 inches (6 to 13 cm); SH 24 to 31.5 inches (60 to 80 cm); W 46 to 112 pounds (21 to 51 kg)
LIFE CYCLE
Mating November to December; gestation about 130 days, two young born

AMERICAN BISON / *Bison bison*

In an 1887 census, the once countless plains bison (*Bison bison bison*) were reduced to 541 individuals by overhunting. Since then, conservation efforts have reestablished this subspecies in Oklahoma and Montana. The other subspecies, the wood bison (*B. bison athabascae*), is listed as endangered. These bovids graze in large herds, preferably on mixed-grass and short-grass prairie. American bison are the largest land mammals native to the western hemisphere, although the females are much smaller than the males. Both sexes have horns. During the breeding season, the males fight over access to the females. Bison share several bacterial infectious diseases with cattle that some ranchers fear may be transmittable to livestock, although studies suggest this is unlikely.

FAMILY
Bovidae
RANGE
Western Canada, northwestern United States
HABITAT
Prairies, open woodlands
SIZE
HB 6.5 to 13 feet (2 to 4 m); T 20 to 24 inches (50 to 60 cm); SH 5 to 6.5 feet (1.5 to 2 m); W 700 to 2,200 pounds (320 to 1,000 kg)
LIFE CYCLE
Mating June to September; gestation 270 to 280 days, one calf born

PRZEWALSKI'S HORSE / *Equus caballus*

This horse is named for the nineteenth-century Russian explorer who first identified the species. It is thought to be the only purebred wild horse still in existence. Originally found over a vast area of desert and steppe in Mongolia and adjacent countries, it may now be extinct in the wild. The last confirmed sighting was in 1968. There are plans to reintroduce zoo-bred animals into its former range. It probably lived in herds of fifteen to twenty mares and young led by one stallion, with separate bachelor herds of up to one hundred. The young are weaned at two years and they live for thirty or so years.

FAMILY
Equidae
RANGE
Formerly Mongolia, southern Siberia, Kazakhstan, and Sinkiang

HABITAT
Desert and steppe
SIZE
HB 7 to 9 feet (2.2 to 2.8 m); T 3 to 4 feet (9 to 11 m); W 440 to 660 pounds (200 to 300 kg)
LIFE CYCLE
Mating in spring or summer; gestation 335 days, one foal born April to June that is weaned at two years of age; maximum life span thirty-four years

PRONGHORN / *Antilocapra americana*

The pronghorn is the fastest North American mammal, capable of sprinting up to forty miles (60 km) per hour and maintaining speeds of thirty miles (45 km) per hour. It lives in small scattered groups in the summer, but in winter herds of up to a hundred may converge, foraging for grasses, weeds, shrubs, and forbs. When a pronghorn is alerted to danger, the white hairs on its rump will stand erect, signaling the others to flee. Both male and female have horns but the male's are larger *(left)*. During breeding season, the male marks its territory with droppings and urine, and violently defends its harem against all rivals.

FAMILY
Antilocapridae
RANGE
Western North America into Mexico
HABITAT
Grassland, open prairie, and desert
SIZE
HB 3 to 5 feet (1 to 1.5 m); T 3 to 4 inches (7 to 10 cm); SH 31.5 to 39 inches (80 to 100 cm); W 77 to 154 pounds (35 to 70 kg)
LIFE CYCLE
Mating September to October, earlier in southern locales; gestation 230 to 250 days, usually two young born

WILD BOAR / *Sus scrofa*

The wild boar, from which the domestic pig is derived, is the most widely distributed pig species; there are sixteen recognized subspecies. Primarily nocturnal animals, they will eat almost anything edible, from tubers to insects and small mammals. They are very strong and can be aggressive, using their tusks as weapons when alarmed. With the decline of such natural predators as wolves and tigers, the number of wild boars has increased, causing problems for farmers in some areas since herds of them can destroy a field of crops in one night as they root through the soil with their snouts in search of bulbs and tubers to eat.

FAMILY
Suidae
RANGE
Europe, northern Africa, Asia; introduced in United States
HABITAT
Grassland and scrub to forest
SIZE
HB 3.5 to 5 feet (1.1 to 1.5 m); T 6 to 8 inches (15 to 20 cm); SH 26 to 31.5 inches (65 to 80 cm); W 143 to 198 pounds (65 to 90 kg)
LIFE CYCLE
Mating varies with locale, November to January in Europe; gestation 110 to 115 days, one to ten piglets born

BLACK-TAILED PRAIRIE DOG / *Cynomys ludovicianus*

The highly social black-tailed prairie dog lives in large subterranean colonies, called townships. The largest reported township was estimated to contain some 400 million residents and to extend twenty-five thousand square miles (65,000 sq km). Townships are divided into wards, which are subdivided into coteries, or harems, composed of one or more adult males, several females, and juveniles. A coterie defends its territory—typically less than one acre (0.5 ha) in size—against other coteries. Diurnal herbivores, prairie dogs spend most of their time above ground, foraging in short- to mid-grass prairie. Their repertoire of calls may include separate

alarm calls for aerial and terrestrial predators. When township density is high, they may kill up to half of the young of close genetic relatives.

FAMILY
Sciuridae
RANGE
Saskatchewan, central United States, and northern Mexico
HABITAT
Prairie
SIZE
HB 11 to 13 inches (28 to 32 cm); T 3 to 4 inches (8.5 to 9.5 cm); W 2 to 3 pounds (0.9 to 1.3 kg)
LIFE CYCLE
Mating February to April; gestation about 30 days, four or five (may be up to ten) young born

PLAINS POCKET GOPHER / *Geomys bursarius*

All pocket gophers are modified for an underground existence: Velvety fur, small ears, and a short tail ease passage in narrow tunnels; long, spade-like claws on sturdy fore limbs aid in digging; a mouth that closes behind the incisor teeth limits ingestion of dirt. Fur of the plains pocket gopher generally matches the soil color. The "pockets" are external fur-lined cheek pouches that may be crammed with food or nesting material. By squeezing with the fore feet, they are emptied and can be turned inside out to be cleaned. The pocket gopher makes an extensive tunnel system, with separate areas for foraging, nesting, and food storage. It eats roots, shoots, and tubers. It is solitary except for a brief period in the breeding season.

FAMILY
Geomyidae
RANGE
Great Plains from Minnesota and North Dakota south to Texas and New Mexico

HABITAT
Prairie, grassland, and agricultural areas
SIZE
HB 5 to 10 inches (14 to 26 cm); T 2 to 4 inches (5 to 10 cm); W 4 to 12 ounces (125 to 350 g)
LIFE CYCLE
Mating in spring; gestation 50 days, one litter of one to seven young born

COMMON HAMSTER / *Cricetus cricetus*

The common hamster, also known as the black-bellied hamster, is quite rare throughout most of Europe. In the wild, it builds an intricate system of burrows where it shelters at night and during the day. Within the burrow are separate food-storage areas and sleeping chambers. Winter burrows are much larger and deeper than summer ones, providing more room to store food and better insulation. Here it hibernates, waking sporadically to feed on caches of food. A solitary creature, it forages in the morning and evening for seeds, grains, insect larvae, and a variety of cultivated crops. The hamster has large, expandable cheek pouches in which to transport food or, when searching for food, to inflate, increasing its buoyancy when it travels across water.

FAMILY
Muridae
RANGE
Western Europe to central Russia
HABITAT
Steppe grassland and cultivated grassy areas
SIZE
HB 9 to 13 inches (24 to 34 cm); T 1 to 2 inches (3 to 6 cm); W 5 to 13 ounces (150 to 380 g)
LIFE CYCLE
Mating April to August; gestation 18 to 20 days, four to twelve young born

SAGEBRUSH VOLE / *Lemmiscus curtatus*

Unlike most voles, which reside in moist habitats, the sagebrush vole lives in arid regions. It prefers to eat the green parts of plants, especially the sagebrush plant, and from late summer through the winter it consumes seeds. It dwells in colonies inside shallow burrows with many entrances and connecting passages. Some burrows contain nests placed at the base of sagebrush plants or other bushy species, and the passages are used as runways to other bushes. It has small ears (larger ones would get in the way of burrowing) and hairy-soled feet to help catch sand and scoop it away. It is active day and night, searching for food and maintaining its burrow. After the female gives birth, she leaves the litter, blocks the burrow entrance, and goes looking for a male to mate. Once she has mated, she returns to nurse her young.

FAMILY
Muridae
RANGE
Southwestern Canada and western United States
HABITAT
Arid and semi-arid grassland
SIZE
HB 4 to 4.5 inches (9.5 to 11.5 cm); T 0.6 to 1.1 inches (1.5 to 3 cm); W 0.7 to 1.4 ounces (20 to 40 g)
LIFE CYCLE
Mating depends on locale; gestation 24 to 25 days, one to thirteen young born; three or more litters per year

MEADOW JUMPING MOUSE / *Zapus hudsonius*

Very long hind feet allow this mouse to make leaps of up to three feet (1 m); the long tail is used for balance when jumping. To elude predators, it may make several long jumps, then freeze. It is mainly nocturnal and solitary in its habits. Its diet changes with the season: In early spring it eats caterpillars and beetles; later it eats the seeds of grasses and weeds as they ripen; in late summer and early fall it favors underground fungi. It eats voraciously before retiring in October to a grass-lined nest to hibernate. Hibernation lasts for six to eight months and it may lose half its body weight during this time. Mice that have not stored enough fat will die during hibernation as they do not wake to feed.

FAMILY
Dipodidae
RANGE
Much of Canada and northeastern United States
HABITAT
Moist fields and brushy areas

SIZE
HB 3 to 4 inches (8 to 10 cm); T 4 to 6 inches (11 to 15 cm); W 0.5 to 1 ounce (14 to 28 g)
LIFE CYCLE
Gestation 19 days, two to nine young born June to August; usually two litters per year

Temperate Forest

The changing colors of maple, beech, and hemlock mark the arrival of autumn in the eastern deciduous forest of Vermont.

There are far fewer species of trees in temperate forests *(map, pages 84 to 85)* than in tropical forests. Broadleafed trees, such as oak, birch, chestnut, and maple, make up most of the trees in the southerly reaches. Farther north, colder temperatures encourage the growth of coniferous trees, such as pine, redwood, hemlock, and cedar.

Seasonal contrasts mark this biome; summers are generally warm, and winters are cold, often below freezing, forcing some mammals to hibernate *(page 10)* or migrate. Rainfall is often more evenly distributed throughout the year, and in some regions, such as northeastern North America and southeastern Australia, the amount is high enough for temperate rain forests to grow.

Although temperate forests are home to a variety of ground-dwelling mammals, including red foxes *(page 153)*, musk deer *(page 154)*, rabbits *(page 159)*, and wild boars *(page 147)*, some forest dwellers have adopted an arboreal lifestyle. Gray squirrels *(page 158)*, for instance, are physically well suited to scampering along branches, gripping the bark with their sharp claws, and jumping from tree to tree, using their tail as a counterbalance. Unlike most tree-climbing mammals, such as bears, which climb down back-end first, these squirrels descend head-first.

North American porcupines *(page 164)*, which live in both the temperate and northern coniferous forests of North America, are also tree climbers, with rough, nonskid pads on the soles of their feet and a tail equipped with modified spines on the underside. Conifers, such as the eastern hemlock, are their food of choice and their passage is often noted by the appearance of shiny rings girdling the trunk high up, where they have eaten the bark away. Other inveterate climbers include the gray fox (*Urocyon cinereoargenteus*), which relies on the extended rotatory ability of its fore legs to help it shinny up trees, while pushing with its hind feet like an arboreal bear. An omnivore, the gray fox generally climbs trees to reach fruit or to escape.

This unusual looking bat gets its common name from the horseshoe-shaped disc that surrounds its nostrils and forms part of the structure it uses to echolocate ground-dwelling insects such as beetles. Its ultrasonic cries are emitted through the nostrils, while the fleshy folds of its skin, including the disc, act as an amplifier. This species spends its days roosting in cavities in hollow trees, caves, and mines. In the fall, it migrates south to reach the caves where it hibernates from October to March. It is not uncommon for thousands of these bats to be seen hibernating together along with other bat species. Because the greater horseshoe bat consumes insects that are considered crop pests, it is of particular importance to humans.

FAMILY
Rhinolophidae
RANGE
Europe, Asia, northern Africa
HABITAT
Forest and woodland
SIZE
HB 2 to 3 inches (6 to 7.5 cm);
T 1.2 to 1.6 inches (3 to 4 cm);
FA 2 to 2.4 inches (5 to 6 cm);
W 0.5 to 1 ounce (13 to 34 g)
LIFE CYCLE
Mating in autumn, fertilization delayed until spring; gestation 65 to 75 days, one young born April to June

The genus *Myotis* is the most widely distributed group of bats; it is only absent from the Arctic, Antarctic, and many of the Oceanic islands. Although occasionally seen flying during the day, *M. nattereri*, like other bats, usually roosts in the daytime and forages for insects at night. After it has flown around for a time catching insects, it returns to its roost to digest its meal before going back out to catch some more. Roosting areas are located in cavities ranging from hollow trees to caves and mines. Once quite common, it is now considered rare in central Europe, where it is threatened by habitat loss.

FAMILY
Vespertilionidae
RANGE
Central and southern Europe, northern Africa, Middle East
HABITAT
Forest and woodland
SIZE
HB 16 to 20 inches (40 to 50 cm); T 1.2 to 1.6 inches (3 to 4 cm); FA about 1.6 inches (4 cm); W 0.2 to 0.4 ounces (5 to 12 g)
LIFE CYCLE
Mating in autumn, fertilization delayed until spring; gestation 50 to 60 days, one young born

BLACK BEAR / *Ursus americanus*

Although black is the most common color of this bear, its color can range from light brown to dark brown. There is even a population of white *Ursus americanus* living on a remote island off the west coast of Canada. A solitary, predominantly vegetarian creature, the black bear uses its keen sense of smell to search out fruit, nuts, berries, and roots. However, this bear will also eat insects, honey, fish, and small mammals when the opportunity arises. It is an excellent tree climber and despite its size regularly ascends to the treetops to eat. From late fall until early spring, the black bear exists in a state of torpor *(page 11)*.

FAMILY
Ursidae
RANGE
Canada, United States, northern Mexico
HABITAT
Forest and woodland

SIZE
HB 4 to 6 feet (1.2 to 1.8 m); T 3.5 to 5 inches (9 to 12.5 cm); SH 24 to 35 inches (60 to 90 cm); W 176 to 500 pounds (80 to 227 kg)
LIFE CYCLE
Mating June to July, implantation delayed until October to November; gestation about 70 days, one to five cubs born; copulation to birth takes about 225 days

RACCOON DOG / *Nyctereuctes procyonoides*

March in a state of lethargy. Because its long, thick fur, known as "ussuri raccoon," has commercial value, the raccoon dog was introduced in Europe, where it spread across much of the continent. Ironically, its fur does not grow as thick or long outside its natural habitat, rendering the fur from Europe virtually worthless.

FAMILY
Canidae
RANGE
Siberia to Japan and northern India; introduced in Europe
HABITAT
Deciduous forest
SIZE
HB 20 to 27 inches (50 to 68 cm); T 5 to 10 inches (13 to 25 cm); W 9 to 22 pounds (4 to 10 kg)
LIFE CYCLE
Mating January to March; gestation 59 to 64 days, four to eight pups born

The raccoon dog is the only canid species that hibernates. A solitary nocturnal forager, it eats a variety of things, including frogs, reptiles, rodents, fish, berries, fruit, and seeds. A particularly abundant food source, such as a fruiting tree or a garbage dump, will attract a whole group of raccoon dogs. In the day, the raccoon dog rests in its burrow, where—in the northern parts of its range—it spends November to

RED FOX / *Vulpes vulpes*

The red fox has the largest geographic distribution of any carnivore in the world. Primarily nocturnal, it is a shy and nervous hunter and scavenger that will eat everything from insects and small mammals to berries and even human garbage. The red fox has acute hearing that can pick up the low-frequency sounds of digging and scraping in underground burrows. When food items are abundant, the fox caches them for harder times. The primary social unit is the mated pair, and their litters are born in dens dug by the adults or taken over from other mammals, such as badgers, and then modified. Older foxes, usually female, help to provision the litter.

FAMILY
Canidae
RANGE
Canada, United States, Europe, Asia, northern Africa
HABITAT
Forest to tundra, including cities
SIZE
HB 24 to 35 inches (60 to 90 cm); T 12 to 22 inches (30 to 55 cm); SH 14 to 16 inches (35 to 41 cm; W 4 to 15 pounds (2 to 7 kg)

LIFE CYCLE
Mating depends on locale, usually January to March; gestation 51 to 63 days, two to ten cubs born

GIANT PANDA / *Ailuropoda melanoleuca*

Reclusive herbivores, giant pandas once enjoyed a wide range in southern China. However, habitat destruction and poaching for their valuable fur have killed off most of them, leaving only about one thousand in the wild. The ancestors of the giant panda were carnivores, but its diet has evolved into one of mostly stalks and roots of the slow-growing, nutrient-poor bamboo. It spends ten to sixteen hours a day eating the twenty to forty pounds (9 to 18 kg) of bamboo it needs for its daily quota. It forages over a large area to get enough; a typical home range is about 1.5 to 2.5 square miles (4 to 6.5 sq km). The solitary panda comes together with others only to mate.

FAMILY
Ailuropodidae
RANGE
Southern central China
HABITAT
Mountains at elevations of 5,000 to 10,000 feet (1,525 to 3,050 m) in bamboo (deciduous) and coniferous forests
SIZE
HB 4 to 6 feet (1.2 to 1.8 m); SH 24 to 32 inches (60 to 80 cm); T 4.5 to 5.5 inches (11.5 to 14 cm); W 165 to 350 pounds (75 to 160 kg)
LIFE CYCLE
Mating March to July, implantation delayed 45 to 120 days; gestation 97 to 163 days, one or two cubs born

RACCOON / *Procyon lotor*

This nocturnal and primarily solitary mammal spends its days sleeping in hollow trees, wedged between branches or, especially in cold weather, in a burrow. An omnivore, it eats both plant parts and animals, such as fish, mollusks, and crustaceans. It was once thought that raccoons washed their food—the scientific name *lotor* means "washer." It is now known that they are pulling food apart to remove inedible bits. The common name derives from the Algonquin word *aroughcoune*, meaning "he scratches with his hands."

FAMILY
Procyonidae
RANGE
Southern Canada to Mexico and Panama; introduced in Asia and Europe
HABITAT
Forest to city, wherever water is available

SIZE
HB 16 to 24 inches (41 to 60 cm); T 8 to 16 inches (20 to 40 cm); SH 9 to 12 inches (22 to 30 cm); W 15 to 44 pounds (7 to 20 kg)
LIFE CYCLE
Mating depends on locale, usually January to May; gestation 60 to 73 days, two to seven young born

SIBERIAN MUSK DEER / *Moschus moschiferus*

Musk deer get their common name from a waxy musk that is produced by a gland on their abdomen. Deer musk is used in perfume and some medicines and is considered by many to be the most valuable animal product in the world. Unlike most other deer, neither sex of musk deer has antlers. Instead, the males have elongated canine teeth that look like tusks, which they use to fight other males to gain access to the females. Usually active in the morning and evenings, musk deer are not often seen, partly because they keep hidden as they forage in dense vegetation for grass, leaves, twigs, flowers, moss, and lichen. All five species are now threatened due to overhunting and habitat destruction.

FAMILY
Moschidae
RANGE
Siberia through Mongolia and Manchuria to Korea

HABITAT
Moist forest
SIZE
HB 28 to 39 inches (71 to 99 cm); SH 20 to 24 inches (51 to 61 cm); W 15 to 40 pounds (7 to 18 kg)
LIFE CYCLE
Mating November to December; gestation 150 to 198 days, usually two fawns born

WAPITI / *Cervus elaphus*

Also called the red deer in Europe and the elk in North America, the wapiti—which means "white rump" in Shawnee—is a gregarious species that typically lives in herds of two hundred or more. Twenty-three widely distributed subspecies are now rec-ognized, predominantly distinguished by size in addition to range differences. Europe has the smallest subspecies, North America the largest. The branched antlers of some North American males are almost six feet (2 m) across. The males use their antlers in autumn fights to defend territory and get access to females.

FAMILY
Cervidae
RANGE
Northwestern North America, north-western Africa, western Europe through Asia to China; introduced in Australia, New Zealand, and Argentina
HABITAT
Forest and woodland
SIZE
HB 5.5 to 9 feet (1.7 to 2.7 m); T 4 to 11 inches (10 to 27 cm); SH 29 to 59 inches (75 to 150 cm); W 165 to 750 pounds (75 to 340 kg)
LIFE CYCLE
Mating September to October, gestation 235 to 265 days, one (rarely two) fawns born

SOUTHERN PUDU / *Pudu pudu*

The pudu is the smallest true deer. Active both in the day and at night, it lives in small herds, feeding mainly on leaves, but also on flowers, fruit, and buds. Because of its diminutive size, it often must stand on its hindlegs, sometimes on top of fallen trees, to reach the foliage. Males are easily distinguished from females by their short straight antlers. The southern pudu is endangered because of overhunting and habitat loss to agriculture and livestock.

FAMILY
Cervidae
RANGE
Southern Chile and southwestern Argentina
HABITAT
Dense lowland forest

SIZE
HB 28 to 33 inches (70 to 83 cm); T 1 to 2 inches (3 to 5 cm); SH 14 to 15 inches (35 to 38 cm); W 16 to 29 pounds (7.5 to 13 kg)
LIFE CYCLE
Mating April to June; gestation 200 to 220 days, one (occasionally two) fawns born

JAPANESE SEROW / *Naemorhedus crispus*

The Japanese serow is primarily a solitary bovid, although pairs and sometimes small family groups may occur. It has a small home range that it marks by rubbing trees and rocks with the smelly secretions from glands located below its eyes and on its hooves. It defends its territory by stabbing with its small horns, which both sexes possess. Sometimes the loser is seriously injured, even mortally. The Japanese serow is ecologically out of balance. Once overhunted, it became so rare that the government of Japan declared it a national treasure. Since then, its numbers have rebounded and it now causes considerable damage to the forests in which it lives. Historically, serow populations were probably kept in check by large predatory cats, which are now all gone.

FAMILY
Bovidae
RANGE
Central and southern Japan
HABITAT
Subalpine forest
SIZE
HB 3 to 5 feet (1 to 1.5 m); T 3 to 6 inches (8 to 16 cm); SH 24 to 29 inches (60 to 75 cm); W 110 to 242 pounds (50 to 110 kg)
LIFE CYCLE
Little is known, believed to mate October to November; gestation about 210 to 225 days, one (sometimes two) fawns born

AMERICAN BEAVER / *Castor canadensis*

The beaver, the second largest rodent in the world (the capybara is the largest), is well known for its wide, flat tail, which it slaps on the surface of the water to warn other beavers of approaching danger. It lives in colonies with four to eight other family members and marks its territory with scent mounds—piles of mud that it scents with glandular secretions. Sometimes it resides in a burrow at the water's edge; more often it lives in a dome-shaped lodge, which it builds with branches and trees cut down with its large incisors. The trees yield bark and leaves, favored foods in winter. In summer it also feeds on other vegetation, especially aquatic plants. It

makes dams to flood areas and bring the trees closer to the water, where it is most comfortable. A secretive and nocturnal creature, it is awkward on land and thus vulnerable to predators.

FAMILY
Castoridae
RANGE
Canada and United States

HABITAT
Streams and lakes in forests
SIZE
HB 27 to 43 inches (70 to 110 cm); T 10 to 16 inches (25 to 40 cm); W 31 to 59 pounds (14 to 27 kg)
LIFE CYCLE
Mating January to February; gestation 105 to 120 days, usually three to five kits born

GARDEN DORMOUSE / *Eliomys quercinus*

The garden dormouse resides in a variety of habitats, including forests, semi-arid steppes, swamps, rocky areas, and montane regions. Its lifestyle ranges from being primarily terrestrial to being highly arboreal, depending on the habitat. It feeds on fruit, insects, and small animals and if hungry will enter houses in search of food. The species is usually solitary, but large, noisy groups sometimes form, sharing sleeping and feeding areas. Winter hibernation helps them survive periods of intense cold and food shortages. When they emerge in the spring, they mate and build nests made of leaves and grasses.

FAMILY
Myoxidae
RANGE
Central and southern Europe to northern Africa
HABITAT
Varied; usually forests

SIZE
HB 4 to 7 inches (10 to 17 cm); T 3.5 to 5 inches (9 to 12 cm); W 2 to 3.5 ounces (50 to 100 g)
LIFE CYCLE
Mating May to June; gestation 22 to 28 days, two to seven young born

EASTERN GRAY SQUIRREL / *Sciurus carolinensis*

The eastern gray squirrel's natural habitat is the hardwood oak, hickory, and walnut forests of eastern North America, where its numbers are controlled by resource availability and predators such as bobcats, owls, and foxes. It was introduced in Britain, where it has become an agricultural pest and out-competed the European red squirrel. The species is a daytime forager, enjoying diverse foods such as pine-cone seeds, nuts, berries, insects, birds' eggs, and occasionally sap from under the bark of new trees. An adult may eat up to three ounces (80 g) of shelled nuts in a day. It stores nuts by burying them in the ground throughout its range, and thus the species is important in the distribution and propagation of trees. It usually makes its nest of leaves in a cavity or crotch of a tree.

FAMILY
Sciuridae
RANGE
Eastern North America; introduced in Britain
HABITAT
Forest and woodland; also cultivated areas and parks
SIZE
HB 9 to 12 inches (23 to 30 cm); T 8 to 9 inches (21 to 23 cm); W 14 to 25 ounces (400 to 700 g)
LIFE CYCLE
Mating December to August; gestation about 40 days, two to five young born

SOUTHERN FLYING SQUIRREL / *Glaucomys volans*

This species, like the sugar glider *(page 99)*, has a flap of skin connecting its front and rear limbs, enabling it to glide in the air. A typical glide ranges from twenty to sixty feet (6 to 18 m) and it can change direction in midair. Strictly nocturnal, these large-eyed squirrels feed primarily on fruit, leaves, insects, nuts, seeds, and birds' eggs. They do not hibernate, but become less active in the winter, feeding on stored nuts and seeds. Their winter dens are usually in tree hollows, which typically shelter three to eight of them, huddling together to keep warm.

FAMILY
Sciuridae
RANGE
Eastern United States through Mexico into Central America
HABITAT
Deciduous forest
SIZE
HB 4.5 to 5 inches (12 to 13.5 cm); T 5 to 6 inches (13 to 15 cm); W 3 to 5 ounces (75 to 140 g)
LIFE CYCLE
Mating February to March; gestation about 40 days, one to six young born; may be more than one litter per year

WHITE-FOOTED MOUSE / *Peromyscus leucopus*

This common nocturnal mouse is often seen climbing in trees, using its long tail for balance. It and the similar-looking deer mouse (*Peromyscus maniculatus*) share many of the same habitats, but the white-footed mouse tends to be found in slightly warmer, drier areas. It eats many types of insects, fruit, nuts, and seeds.

When food is abundant, the mouse may cache it in cavities or bury it close to the nest. Nests are built out of grass, feathers, bark, and other materials. Although in captivity it may live several years, in the wild there is usually a complete replacement of the population each year. Most die in spring and early summer, perhaps because of greater predation, typically by larger mammals, birds, and snakes.

FAMILY
Muridae
RANGE
Southern Canada, central and eastern United States
HABITAT
Forest and woodland
SIZE
HB 3.5 to 4 inches (9 to 11 cm); T 2.4 to 4 inches (6 to 10 cm); W 0.3 to 1 ounce (10 to 30 g)
LIFE CYCLE
Mating spring to fall; gestation 22 to 23 days, usually four to five young born; two to four litters per year

WOODLAND VOLE / *Microtus pinetorum*

Woodland voles prefer areas with loose sandy soils or a thick layer of soft humus or leafy mold because they are primarily subterranean burrowers, only rarely coming to the surface. They forage on nuts, seeds, fresh leaves, and insects and their larvae and store food in underground caches. They tend to be colonial, but colonies may form and disperse for no apparent reason.

Groups of up to fifteen individuals containing adult males, females, and their offspring may be associated with a single tunnel system, which can be recognized by the heaps of soil around the burrow's openings above ground. Predators include predatory birds such as owls and hawks, as well as foxes, opossums, and snakes.

FAMILY
Muridae
RANGE
Southern Ontario and eastern United States
HABITAT
Deciduous forests and orchards
SIZE
HB 3 to 4 inches (7 to 11 cm); T 0.8 to 1 inch (2 to 2.5 cm); W 0.7 to 1.4 ounces (20 to 40 g)
LIFE CYCLE
Mating varies by locale, throughout year in south, gestation 20 to 24 days, one to six young born

EUROPEAN RABBIT / *Oryctolagus cuniculus*

Domesticated rabbits are derived from this species of lagomorph. It lives in colonies and is frequently found sharing multichambered burrows with several individuals. It feeds on grasses, weeds, buds, sprouts, and, in winter, bark. When alarmed, it loudly thumps the ground with its hind foot to warn of approaching danger. The young are born in a special burrow lined with soft fur and located away from the rest of the colony. Originally from North Africa and Spain, the species was introduced in Europe in ancient times, and more recently elsewhere around the world, especially Australia and New Zealand, where it is considered an agricultural pest.

FAMILY
Leporidae
RANGE
Europe and throughout world
HABITAT
Woodland to grassland and sandy, scrubby areas
SIZE
HB 14 to 18 inches (35 to 45 cm); T 2 to 3 inches (4 to 7 cm); W 3 to 5 pounds (1 to 2 kg)
LIFE CYCLE
Mating usually December to May, may be year-round; gestation 28 to 33 days, three to nine young born; usually three or four litters per year

Northern Coniferous Forest

One of the largest concentrations of trees on Earth, the northern, or boreal, forest extends across North America and northern Eurasia *(map, pages 84 to 85)*. The ecology of this vast landscape of pine, spruce, fir, and larch rarely attains a climax or stable state because of the biome's long winter, short growing season, and frequent natural forest fires.

Some mammal species that inhabit boreal forests also live farther south, but in the north, these species tend to be larger. Their greater size helps them conserve energy, especially in winter, a significant adaptation that outweighs the disadvantage of requiring more food to sustain a larger bulk.

The threat of food shortages dominates the life of most mammals living in the north. The moose *(page 163)* and the caribou *(page 168)*, for instance, rarely stop foraging in the winter, looking for alternate food sources—aquatic plants in the case of the moose, tundra lichen for the caribou—that are covered by ice and snow. Heavy grazing and digging of forest lichen and new shoots and saplings puts pressure on a forest's ecology. This, coupled with fire damage, sometimes results in serious food shortages and a subsequent decline in the region's moose and caribou populations.

Survival strategies of smaller boreal mammals include hibernation *(page 11)* or, as with many rodents, wintertime burrowing under the thick blanket of snow, where mosses, herbs, and shrubs remain available. Predators such as the marten *(page 162)* and the mink *(Mustela vison)* face the winter with pelages of thick underfur and long, stiff guard hairs.

Coniferous trees thrive on the shores of Siberia's Lake Baikal. Their needles are well suited to the cold, dry climate of the taiga, or boreal forest; the narrow shape of the needles reduces moisture loss and because they remain on the tree year-round, they are ready to resume photosynthesis as soon as the short growing season arrives.

MASKED SHREW / *Sorex cinereus*

This tiny mammal has one of the largest ranges of all North American mammals, yet because it is nocturnal and very small, it is almost never seen. During the day, it sleeps in leafy nests under logs and rocks and in clumps of grass. It spends most of its waking time rooting about in the leaf litter in search of food, consuming the

equivalent of its own body weight every day. Its diet consists primarily of invertebrates, such as caterpillars and their larvae, spiders, and snails, but also includes small vertebrates and seeds. It does not hibernate in the winter; instead it spends its nights searching for dormant insects.

FAMILY
Soricidae
RANGE
Alaska, Canada, northern
United States
HABITAT
Moist habitats from forest
to tundra
SIZE
HB 2 to 2.5 inches (5 to 6 cm);
T 1 to 2 inches (3 to 5 cm);
W 0.1 to 0.3 ounce (3 to 8 g)
LIFE CYCLE
Mating depends on local conditions,
usually April to September; gestation
19 to 21 days, two to ten young born

FISHER / *Martes pennanti*

The fisher is primarily nocturnal, but will occasionally venture out during the day. Usually it spends the day sleeping inside hollow trees or logs. It is aggressive and will eat just about anything it can kill, especially small mammals, birds, fish, and insects. It is one of the few carnivores that preys on porcupine *(page 156)*. When

the porcupine takes refuge in trees, the fisher follows. Because it is able to descend trees headfirst, the fisher attacks the porcupine from above, biting its face—one of the few places without spines—and avoiding its quills. It may gorge itself for two days on the carcass of one porcupine.

FAMILY
Mustelidae
RANGE
Canada and northern
United States
HABITAT
Coniferous forest
SIZE
HB 20 to 27 inches (50 to
70 cm); T 12 to 16 inches
(30 to 42 cm); W 3 to 8
pounds (1.5 to 8 kg)
LIFE CYCLE
Mating March to May, implantation delayed until January
to March; gestation about 30
days, one to six young born

PINE MARTEN / *Martes martes*

by a single individual, which will store numerous caches of food throughout its home range. This species is highly valued for its supple coat and has disappeared in many parts of its original range due to centuries of overhunting.

FAMILY
Mustelidae
RANGE
Europe and Asia
HABITAT
Coniferous, deciduous, and mixed woodlands

This agile climber is most active during evenings and mornings, when it hunts a variety of animals, including birds, squirrels, small rodents, hares, and insects. It also forages for fruit. When chasing prey in the trees, it jumps quickly from branch to branch, using its claws for gripping. During the day, it shelters in nests in hollow trees. Several nests are often utilized

SIZE
HB 18 to 23 inches (45 to 58 cm); T 6 to 11 inches (16 to 28 cm); W 2 to 4 pounds (1 to 2 kg)
LIFE CYCLE
Mating July to August, implantation delayed; pregnancy 230 to 275 days, usually three to five young born

SABLE / *Martes zibellina*

Sables are valued commercially for their beautiful, long, silky winter pelage. However, hunting restrictions, captive rearing, and reintroductions have prevented this species from becoming endangered. It is active both during the day and at night as it travels in search of food such as small rodents, fish, birds, berries, and nuts. Most

of its time is spent on the ground, but it will climb trees, especially in pursuit of prey. It has a relatively large home range and often has many dens in hollow logs, under rock piles, or in burrows, thus enabling it to move about more easily. Territories are well defended, but may overlap or be shared with a female.

FAMILY
Mustelidae
RANGE
Northern Europe and Asia
HABITAT
Coniferous forests and woodlands
SIZE
HB 13 to 23 inches (32 to 58 cm); T 3 to 7 inches (9 to 19 cm); W 2 to 4 pounds (1 to 2 kg)
LIFE CYCLE
Mating June to August, implantation delayed 210 to 240 days; gestation 25 to 40 days, one to seven young born

GRAY WOLF / *Canis lupus*

The largest canid in the world, the gray wolf spends most of its life in packs, usually of five to ten individuals, that are led by the so-called alpha pair, the only male and female in the pack to breed. Occasionally the wolf hunts and forages alone. However, when preying on large animals such as moose and deer, it will hunt with the pack, using a variety of strategies, such as pushing its prey toward a rendez-vous point where other pack members wait in ambush. The wolf uses a haunting howl to keep the pack together. High-ranking adults also communicate by scent-marking with urine and feces.

FAMILY
Canidae
RANGE
Canada and northern United States; southern and eastern Europe to India and Russia
HABITAT
Varied: forest, grassland, tundra
SIZE
HB 3 to 5 feet (1 to 1.6 m); T 12 to 20 inches (30 to 50 cm); SH 20 to 39 inches (50 to 100 cm); W 50 to 176 pounds (23 to 80 kg)
LIFE CYCLE
Mating January to March; gestation 61 to 63 days, three to seven cubs born

MOOSE / *Alces alces*

Moose, known in Europe as elk, are the largest members of the deer family; they also have the largest antlers. Found only on males, these palmate antlers may measure as much as six feet (2 m) across and weigh up to seventy pounds (32 kg). They are shed and regrown annually. The males use their antlers to fight each other during rutting season. The moose is rarely gregarious, except when a harem forms during mating season. A ruminant with a four-chambered stomach, the moose feeds on leaves, twigs, and young shoots of trees, as well as aquatic plants.

FAMILY
Cervidae
RANGE
Northern North America, Europe, and Asia
HABITAT
Coniferous forests around marshes and bogs
SIZE
HB 8 to 10 feet (2.4 to 3.1 m); T 2 to 6 inches (5 to 15 cm); SH 5 to 8 feet (1.4 to 2.4 m); W 730 to 1,810 pounds (330 to 820 kg)
LIFE CYCLE
Mating August to October; gestation 230 to 260 days, usually one calf born

NORTH AMERICAN PORCUPINE / *Erethizon dorsatum*

When threatened, a porcupine turns away from its attacker and erects the quills on its back; upright, they detach easily if they are touched (or bitten). The porcupine may also back up and swing its tail for additional force. These solitary nocturnal creatures feed on leaves, berries, roots, seeds, twigs, and bark. Adept climbers, they ascend trees for food, to escape predators, and to sleep. The female's estrus lasts from eight to twelve hours and the normally sedentary male searches for her by her smell. Their courtship is accompanied by loud screeches, and the male mounts her carefully from behind, a mating position adopted by most mammals.

FAMILY
Erethizontidae
RANGE
Alaska, Canada, western United States, and northern Mexico

HABITAT
Forest to desert
SIZE
HB 18 to 25 inches (46 to 63 cm); T 5.5 to 12 inches (14 to 30 cm); W 9 to 40 pounds (4 to 18 kg)
LIFE CYCLE
Mating September to November; gestation 200 to 217 days, one (sometimes two) young born

RED SQUIRREL / *Tamiasciurus hudsonicus*

The red squirrel is a noisy creature: When courting, it makes a "buzz" sound similar to that of a cicada; it chatters to warn off other red squirrels and competitors; and when displaying aggression against intruders, it makes a charac-teristic bark. The red squirrel gener-ally nests in tree cavities and in holes in the ground, although it also shelters in exposed spherical nests of grass, leaves, and twigs. It prefers conifer seeds; mid-dens of scales left from stripping the cones are a common sign of its presence. It does not hiber-nate, but instead lives on stored supplies through the winter. Females are receptive to males for only one day each breeding season; males are rebuffed at other times. Many predators, such as red foxes, fishers, and martens, depend on red squirrels for food.

FAMILY
Sciuridae
RANGE
Canada, northern and mountain ranges in south-west United States
HABITAT
Coniferous forest, mixed coniferous and deciduous woodland
SIZE
HB 6.5 to 9 inches (16.5 to 23 cm); T 3.5 to 6 inches (9 to 16 cm); W about 9 ounces (250 g)
LIFE CYCLE
Mating February to September, two seasonal peaks; gestation 33 to 38 days, two to six young born

NORTHERN RED-BACKED VOLE / *Clethrionomys rutilis*

The northern red-backed vole does not hibernate, but remains active all winter, feeding on the seeds, nuts, and roots that it gathered during warmer weather. In the tundra, where it is also found, it tends to be larger, with a redder pelage than here in the boreal forest. Once the snow has melted, the population of *Clethrionomys rutilis* is made up entirely of those born the year before, but within about eight weeks, the first of the young are starting to breed. By the end of summer, all those born the year before have died. Its abundance makes the northern red-backed vole popular prey for weasels and other small carnivores, as well as predatory birds.

Another name for it is the polar red-backed vole, and Laplanders call it the squirrel mouse.

FAMILY
Muridae
RANGE
Northern North America and Eurasia
HABITAT
Coniferous forest to tundra
SIZE
HB 4 to 5 inches (11 to 12 cm);
T 1.1 to 1.4 inches (2.8 to 3.6 cm);
W 0.7 to 1.3 ounce (20 to 40 g)
LIFE CYCLE
Mating May to September; gestation 17 to 19 days, four to nine young born; two to five litters per year

YELLOW-CHEEKED VOLE / *Microtus xanthognathus*

Also called the taiga vole, the yellow-cheeked vole is the largest of the meadow voles in the genus *Microtus*, which means "small ears." It makes extensive runways for traveling from burrow to feeding area, some on the surface in leaf litter and some below ground. It is usually active around dusk, feeding on grass, fruit, horsetails, and sometimes lichens. It lives in communal nests with up to seven openings along a shallow burrow system. A male's territory usually overlaps with the home ranges of several females. Voles mark their territory with the secretions of glands located in their flanks. When danger approaches, one will give a warning call; others will often join in as a predator passes through the area. Like other voles, their populations fluctuate from year to year, with density reaching a maximum of about one hundred yellow-cheeked voles per 2.5 acres (1 ha).

FAMILY
Muridae
RANGE
Alaska to Manitoba

HABITAT
Coniferous forests, often close to marshes and bogs
SIZE
HB 5 to 7 inches (13 to 17 cm); T about 2 inches (5 cm); W 3.5 to 6 ounces (100 to 170 g)
LIFE CYCLE
Mating spring to late summer; gestation 20 to 22 days, up to ten young born; may have multiple litters per year

Tundra

Finnish for "barren land," tundra *(map, pages 84 to 85)* is a band of sparsely covered land bordered by boreal forests to the south, permanent ice to the north. Bitterly cold, dark winters and minimal precipitation make life difficult here. Summers are brief, but the long hours of daylight nourish a mantle of plants that help support wildlife.

Within the tundra, there are three distinct vegetation divisions. The southern tundra, also called the low arctic, sustains woody plants, including scrubby willow and birch, and poorly drained soil creates extensive bogs. In the middle arctic, dwarfed woody plants grow close to the ground to avoid strong winds. In the high arctic, moss and lichen, as well as some hardy herbs, cling to bare rock. Few mammals live this far north, and those that do, such as the polar bear *(page opposite)* have

had to make significant adaptations to survive the cold.

The mammals of the tundra include both migrants and residents. Among the migrants, the caribou *(page 168)* stand out. Large herds still make the journey of several hundred miles from their winter habitat in the coniferous forests farther south to spring and summer grazing grounds on the tundra.

Resident mammals rarely hibernate because the summer isn't long enough to accumulate sufficient fat reserves. Instead, burrowing under the snow has been perfected, particularly by the collared lemming *(page 169)*. The lemming is also the only rodent with a pelage that changes to an all-white winter coat. Other tundra residents that change color with the snow include the arctic fox *(page opposite)* and the arctic hare *(page 169)*.

One of the largest caribou herds in the world—numbering 750,000 at last count—roams the wooded tundra around Quebec's Georges River. Two-thirds of their diet is made up of this region's rich supply of lichens, slow-growing plants that consist of a symbiotic relationship of algae (usually green) and fungi.

ARCTIC FOX / *Alopex lagopus*

A shortened snout and tiny round ears (smallest among foxes) help the arctic fox reduce heat loss, hair on the soles of its feet insulate against the cold ground, and a very thick winter fur keeps it so warm that it doesn't begin to shiver until the temperature drops to about minus ninety degrees Fahrenheit (-70°C). This fox is the only canid with a coat that changes color seasonally; its winter coat is white and its summer coat is blue-gray or gray-brown. A nocturnal burrower, the arctic fox is occasionally seen by day hunting small mammals. Its diet also includes birds and their eggs, carrion, and berries. In years when food is scarce, arctic fox populations decline and no young are produced.

FAMILY
Canidae
RANGE
Arctic and tundra of North America, Europe, and Asia
HABITAT
Tundra
SIZE
HB 20 to 27 inches (50 to 70 cm); T 12 to 16 inches (30 to 40 cm); SH 9 to 11 inches (22 to 27.5 cm; W 7 to 18 pounds (3 to 8 kg)
LIFE CYCLE
Mating May to June; gestation 49 to 57 days, usually three or four kits born

POLAR BEAR / *Ursus maritimus*

The semi-aquatic polar bear was once considered to be nomadic, but has since been shown to have a very large home range—up to about 115 square miles (300 sq km). Pregnant bears den in the winter, the others hunt. Ringed seals are their preferred prey, but in winter, they will eat anything they can catch; in summer, they will eat leaves, berries, and seaweed. They are able to fast for months, drawing on stored fat at any time of the year. Their hairs are hollow, making for excellent insulators that are capable of trapping much of their radiating body heat. Only the nose and eyes radiate heat, so they cover them with their paws when they sleep.

FAMILY
Ursidae
RANGE
Above Arctic Circle, occasionally farther south
HABITAT
Coastal regions and ice floes
SIZE
HB 7 to 9 feet (2.2 to 2.8 m); T 3 to 5 inches (8 to 13 cm); SH about 5 feet (1.5 m); W 660 to 1,540 pounds (300 to 700 kg)
LIFE CYCLE
Mating April to May, implantation delayed until September to October; one to three cubs born in December

CARIBOU / *Rangifer tarandus*

Known in Europe and Asia as reindeer, the caribou is the only species of deer in which both sexes bear antlers. Males lose them in the spring; females lose them when they give birth in June. Eight subspecies are recognized, each varying in size, shape, and color. Huge herds spend the winter feeding in boreal forests. In the spring, they migrate hundreds of miles north to calving grounds in the tundra. They wander all summer, feeding on leaves of small shrubs, aromatic plants, grasses, sedges, fungi, and lichens; in the fall, they breed. In Europe, they have been domesticated and are used to pull sleighs since their broad hooves are suited for walking in deep snow.

FAMILY
Cervidae
RANGE
Northern Europe, northern Asia, northern Canada, and Alaska
HABITAT
Arctic tundra
SIZE
HB 4 to 7 feet (1.2 to 2.2 m); T 4 to 8 inches (10 to 20 cm); SH 34 to 55 inches (87 to 140 cm); W 130 to 700 pounds (60 to 318 kg)
LIFE CYCLE
Mating September to November; gestation 220 to 240 days, usually one (maybe two) calves born; twins more likely in Europe

MUSKOX / *Ovibos moschatus*

The male muskox emits a strong musky odor during the mating season. At this time of year, the male is very aggressive, clashing with other males to keep them away from his small harem. Rivals charge each other at a gallop, smashing their heads together. Fortunately, their skulls are protected by massive helmets of horn, or bosses. Females have bosses and horns, too. Muskox feed on the leaves of small shrubs, grass, sedges, herbs, moss, and lichen. When threatened by predators such as wolves and bears, they form a circle or a crescent facing the attack, with the young and females protected in the center.

FAMILY
Bovidae
RANGE
Northern Canada, especially arctic islands; also western Greenland
HABITAT
Arctic tundra
SIZE
HB 6 to 8 feet (1.8 to 2.5 m); T 4 to 5.5 inches (10 to 14 cm); SH about 5 feet (1.5 m); W 400 to 840 pounds (180 to 380 kg)
LIFE CYCLE
Mating July to September; gestation 230 to 260 days, one (rarely two) calves born

COLLARED LEMMING / *Dicrostonyx torquatus*

The collared lemming nests in small tunnels in the tundra's soft, mossy-herb carpet. In winter, it digs down under the snow and makes a large nest, about ten inches (25 cm) wide, which it fills with cotton grasses. Its most distinctive feature is a split digging claw on its third and fourth digit. During the winter, this claw becomes longer and stronger to facilitate digging in the ice and frozen ground. The pelage of the collared lemming is brown in summer and white in winter, providing camouflage in the snow.

FAMILY
Cricetidae
RANGE
Northeastern Europe and Siberia
HABITAT
Tundra
SIZE
HB 5 to 6 inches (12 to 15 cm);
T 0.4 to 0.8 inch (1 to 2 cm);
W 1.8 to 3.5 ounces (50 to 100 g)
LIFE CYCLE
Mating March to September;
gestation 19 to 21 days, one
to eleven young born

ARCTIC HARE / *Lepus arcticus*

The average temperature where the arctic hare lives is minus twenty-two degrees Fahrenheit (-30°C). A specialized thick fur coat insulates it, while short ears reduce heat loss and densely furred feet help prevent sinking in the snow. In addition, it possesses strong claws for digging through snow and ice. It prefers to eat woody plants of various types, especially willow. It generally shelters in a depression on the ground, sometimes with one or more companions, but during severe winter weather it will dig a tunnel to escape the cold. Social groups consisting of ten to sixty individuals are common, and sometimes herds of several thousand form on arctic islands. Arctic hares can hop up to forty miles (60 km) or so per hour, outrunning most potential predators. During the breeding season, males become aggressive, slashing out at other males or boxing with their fore feet. The females give birth to young in a shallow depression lined with moss and grass, and after a couple of weeks they deposit the young in a communal nursery containing up to twenty offspring.

FAMILY
Leporidae
RANGE
Northern Canada
and Greenland
HABITAT
Rocky slopes and
tundra regions
SIZE
HB 19 to 26 inches (48 to
67 cm); T 1 to 3 inches
(3 to 8 cm); W 6 to 15
pounds (3 to 7 kg)
LIFE CYCLE
Mating early April; gestation
about 50 days, two to eight
young born

Marine

The oceans cover more than two-thirds of the globe *(map, pages 84 to 85)*, providing a home for at least 118 species of mammals. To make their living there, these mammals have to be able to suspend their breathing for lengthy periods. The capacity of seals and cetaceans for carrying oxygen is higher than land mammals because their blood contains twice the number of red blood cells. This, along with a circulatory system that diverts blood from other parts of the body to the heart and brain, permits them to carry out protracted dives. Cetaceans can also slow down their heart rate during long dives; some whales may remain submerged for almost two hours. To survive in the coldest regions of the ocean, fur-covered marine mammals such as the harp seal *(page opposite)* make use of air trapped in the fur as an added layer of insulation. Small mammals also employ vasoconstriction, reducing blood flow to the limbs to keep the body core and vital organs at a constant temperature. Large cetaceans such as the sperm whale *(page 173)* keep warm with an enormous shell of insulating blubber. When they need to cool down, they draw in ocean water through the blow hole and circulate it through nasal passages, cooling the capillaries in the adjacent spermaceti organ of the head, effectively cooling the whale's whole body. The heated water is then expelled from the blow hole.

 WALRUS / *Odobenus rosmarus*

Walruses have enlarged upper canine teeth, or tusks, up to three feet (1 m) long. They feed on invertebrates such as crustaceans, starfish, and mollusks, which they suck out of the shell. They also prey on fish and seals. The walrus uses its tusks to chop breathing holes in ice and to get from water onto floes, jabbing the ice as it hoists up its body. In struggles for dominance, the male displays his tusks. Usually the behavior is limited to posturing, but violence can ensue, with a walrus striking his tusks point-first into his opponent. Adult males develop hide thickenings on the neck and shoulders, perhaps due to scarring from such battles.

FAMILY
Odobenidae
RANGE
Circumpolar in north

HABITAT
Shallow coastal water and ice floes
SIZE
TL 7.5 to 12 feet (2.3 to 3.6 m); W 1,300 to 3,300 pounds (600 to 1,500 kg)
LIFE CYCLE
Mating January to March, implantation delayed 90 to 120 days; gestation 310 to 335 days, one (rarely two) young born

HARP SEAL / *Phoca groenlandica*

Harp seals migrate in large groups as much as five thousand miles (8,000 km) from feeding grounds in the north to breeding grounds in the south. They spend about half the year in the north, feeding on fish and invertebrates. In the spring, thousands of females congregate on pack ice to give birth and nurse their white-furred pups. Following weaning, the pups shed their white fur, which is replaced by silver-gray pelage with dark spots. After successive molts, the spots are replaced by the typical harp-shaped marking on the back. By June the harp seals are moving northward again, swimming and cavorting in the frigid water. There are three populations of this gregarious seal: one off Newfoundland, one in the Arctic Ocean, and one off Greenland.

FAMILY
Phocidae
RANGE
Northern Atlantic and Arctic oceans
HABITAT
Arctic waters and ice floes
SIZE
TL 4.6 to 6.6 feet (1.4 to 2 m); W 220 to 320 pounds (100 to 145 kg)
LIFE CYCLE
Mating February to April, implantation delayed 60 to 90 days; gestation 210 to 240 days, one pup born

LEOPARD SEAL / *Hydrurga leptonyx*

This seal gets its common name from the numerous dark spots on its coat; the name leopard seal, though, is sometimes also applied to other spotted seals, such as the Weddell's seal. A solitary seal, it has huge canine teeth and massive jaws. Generally it feeds on krill, which it strains from the water with its specialized teeth. It is the only seal that preys on warm-blooded animals; it catches penguins and even other seals, which it pursues underwater. A fast swimmer, it also preys on fish and squid.

FAMILY
Phocidae

RANGE
Antarctic ocean and shores; occasionally along coasts of South America, South Africa, Australia, and New Zealand
HABITAT
Coastal waters and shores
SIZE
TL 8 to 12 feet (2.4 to 3.6 m); W 440 to 990 pounds (200 to 450 kg)
LIFE CYCLE
Mating November to February, implantation believed delayed about 60 days; gestation 250 to 270 days, one pup born

STRIPED DOLPHIN / *Stenella coeruleoalba*

Identified by the lateral stripes that originate at their eyes, the striped dolphins are sometimes seen swimming alongside large ships off California and in the Atlantic, a behavior known as bow-riding. In the eastern tropical Pacific, where they are also found, they tend to be shyer. These dolphins are energetic swimmers, sometimes moving upside down and jumping as high as twenty feet (6 m) out of the water to do backward somersaults. Social animals, they are commonly found in schools of up to five hundred individuals. The size of the school depends on geographic location; those from the western Pacific, where they are more abundant, tend to be much larger than the groups in the eastern Atlantic Ocean. Schools may be classified according to age and breeding status.

FAMILY
Delphinidae

RANGE
Temperate, subtropical, and tropical oceans
HABITAT
Oceans
SIZE
TL 6 to 8 feet (1.8 to 2.5 m); W 200 to 330 pounds (90 to 150 kg)
LIFE CYCLE
Mating in autumn; gestation 330 to 360 days, one young born

 HARBOR PORPOISE / *Phocoena phocoena*

Harbor porpoises acquired their common name because they tend to swim close to land and the females bring their young into bays to nurse. More often heard than seen, the harbor porpoise makes a sneezelike sound when it blows— which has led to another common name, "puffing pig." It is often found in groups composed of from two to ten animals, although larger temporary groups may form for feeding. Fish make up the majority of its diet, especially mackerel, herring, cod, and sardines, which it hunts by echolocation. It reaches maturity at three to five years of age and can live until thirteen years old. Today the species is threatened because they get entangled in bottom gillnets used for fishing.

FAMILY
Phocoenidae

RANGE
Northern Atlantic and Pacific oceans, Black and Mediterranean seas
HABITAT
Shallow waters and estuaries
SIZE
TL 4.6 to 6 feet (1.4 to 1.8 m); W 99 to 143 pounds (45 to 65 kg)
LIFE CYCLE
Mating June to August; gestation 300 to 330 days, one young born

GREAT SPERM WHALE / *Physeter catodon*

Great sperm whales are the biggest of all toothed whales, the males usually much larger than the females. They travel in pods of up to fifty, composed of one or two males and a harem. Their common name is derived from a structure in their head known as the spermaceti organ, which is filled with a liquid waxy substance often referred to as sperm oil. It is thought that this structure helps control buoyancy during dives—recorded to depths of sixty-five hundred feet (2,000 m), but typically less than half this. When they dive, they use sonar to search for squid, their primary food source. The spermaceti organ may also play a part in sonar reception. Because of heavy hunting, fewer than 200,000 of the whales are estimated to remain.

FAMILY
Physeteridae
RANGE
Oceans worldwide
HABITAT
Temperate and tropical oceans
SIZE
TL 39 to 59 feet (12 to 18 m); W 44,000 to 110,000 pounds (20,000 to 50,000 kg)
LIFE CYCLE
Mating usually January to August; gestation 450 to 400 days, usually one calf born

NORTHERN RIGHT WHALE / *Eubalaena glacialis*

Right whales are primarily solitary animals, although sometimes they are found in pairs. The growths, or callosities, on their head are distinctive enough to identify individuals. They move slowly through the water with their mouth partially agape, straining plankton with their baleen plates. Only about three hundred to six hundred of them still exist because of overhunting for centuries for their oil, meat, and baleen (whalebone). Their common name stems from their being the "right" whale to hunt: They were among the most valuable of whales; they swim slowly, close to shore; and once killed, their carcasses float, or "right" themselves.

FAMILY
Balaenidae
RANGE
Northern Pacific and Atlantic oceans

HABITAT
Coastal waters
SIZE
TL 36 to 59 feet (11 to 18 m); W 66,000 to 180,000 pounds (30,000 to 80,000 kg)
LIFE CYCLE
Mating February to April; gestation 365 days, one calf born

BLUE WHALE / *Balaenoptera musculus*

Blue whales are the biggest animals in the world, and the females are larger than the males. The longest female on record measured 110 feet (34 m); the heaviest weighed 190 tons. All three subspecies travel in pods composed of thirty to fifty individuals. These whales, as with other members of the family Balaenopteridae, filter some six to seven tons of krill at a time with their baleen plates, "gulping" water and krill, then closing the mouth and forcing the water back out through the baleen. Blue whales were too big and too fast for whalers before the 1864 invention of the exploding-head harpoon. That and the indiscriminate use of factory ships have led to the species' rapid decline. Now fewer than ten thousand remain.

FAMILY
Balaenopteridae
RANGE
All major oceans of world
HABITAT
Open ocean
SIZE
TL 79 to 89 feet (24 to 27 m);
W 220,000 to 330,000 pounds
(100,000 to 150,000 kg);
historically much larger
LIFE CYCLE
Mating depends on locale; gestation
300 to 330 days, one calf born

WEST INDIAN MANATEE / *Trichechus manatus*

The manatee, often called the sea cow, is the only exclusively herbivorous marine mammal. It grazes on all kinds of aquatic plants, especially marine sea grasses, assisted by its large prehensile lips, which are studded with bristles. During the day, it is frequently found close to the surface, sleeping within the top three to ten feet (1 to 3 m). Occasionally it swims down to thirty feet (10 m), propelling itself along with the aid of its large flat tail, which it also uses as a rudder. When feeding, which it usually does at night, it walks along the bottom using its fore limbs. It is restricted to tropical and subtropical waters because it has an unusually low metabolic rate for a large mammal and rapidly loses body heat to the surrounding water. Because it was overhunted in the past and—despite its current protected status—continues to be caught in fishing gear and hit by speed boats, the West Indian manatee is endangered.

FAMILY
Trichechidae
RANGE
Florida to northeastern
Brazil, including islands
HABITAT
Rivers, estuaries, and
coastal waters
SIZE
TL 8 to 13 feet (2.4 to 4 m);
W 440 to 1,300 pounds
(200 to 600 kg)
LIFE CYCLE
Mating year-round; gestation
385 to 400 days, one (sometimes two) calves born

RESOURCE GUIDE

This guide contains a selection of addresses and websites of wildlife associations, zoos, parks, and reserves (pages 176 to 179) from around the world. Also found here is a brief summary of mammal taxonomy (page 180) and a selection of some of the world's most endangered mammals (page 181). Finally, a glossary of mammal terms is presented on pages 182 to 183.

International Directory

URLs Only

Australian A to Z Animal Archive
Complete listing of Australian fauna, including information and photos
http://aaa.com.au/A_Z/

Elephant Information Repository
Species information; conservation; multimedia; links
http://elephant.elehost.com/

Eurobats
Features on European bats; conservation news
enquiry@eurobats.org
http://www.eurobats.org/

Geo Zoo: Mammals!
Species profiles; features; photos; book selections; links
http://www.geobop.com/Mammals/

Global Zoo Directory
Comprehensive listing of zoos
http://www.cbsg.org/gzd.htm

Major Biomes of the World (Geography Department, Radford University, Virginia)
Information on all terrestrial biomes
http://www.runet.edu/~swoodwar/CLASSES/GEOG235/biomes/main.html

Museum of Paleontology, University of California at Berkeley (UCMP): Hall of Mammals
Access to extensive archives, including an encyclopedia of mammals
http://www.ucmp.berkeley.edu/index.html

Tour of Biomes
Information on all terrestrial biomes
http://www.cotf.edu/ete/modules/msese/earthsysflr/biomes.html

University of Michigan Animal Diversity Web
http://www.ummz.lsa.umich.edu/

U.S. Fish and Wildlife Service
Endangered species; news releases; maps; special programs; links
http://www.fws.gov/

World Wildlife Federation (WWF)
Endangered species; research information; news features; photos; multi-media
http://www.panda.org/

ASSOCIATIONS, JOURNALS, AND RESEARCH CENTERS

American Society of Mammalogists
Publisher, Journal of Mammalogy
H. Duane Smith, Secretary-Treasurer
Monte L. Bean Museum
Brigham Young University
Provo, UT 84602
Duane@museum.byu.edu
http://asm.wku.edu/mammalsinfo.html

American Zoo and Aquarium Association
Suite 710, 8403 Colesville Road
Silver Spring, MD 20910
Tel: (301) 562-0777-234
Fax: (301) 562-0888
membership@aza.org.
http://www.aza.org/

Australian Mammal Society
Publisher, Australian Mammalogy
Department of Environment and Natural Resources
Adelaide, SA
Australia
sgibbs@picknowl.com.au
http://ikarus.jcu.edu.au/mammal/

BIOSIS U.K.
Publisher, The Zoological Record
Garforth House
54 Micklegate
York, YO1 6WF
United Kingdom
Tel: +44 (0) 1904-642816
Fax: +44 (0) 1904-612793
helpdesk@york.biosis.org
http://www.york.biosis.org

International Marine Mammal Project
Information; conservation; photos
Suite 28, 300 Broadway
San Francisco, CA 94133
Tel: (415) 788-3666
marinemammal@earthisland.org
http://www.earthisland.org/immp/dolphin.htm

International Primate Protection League
Conservation; membership
U.S. address:
P.O. Box 766
Summerville, SC 29484
Tel: (843) 871-2280
U.K. address:
116 Judd Street
London, WC1H9NS
ippl@awod.com
http://www.ippl.org/index.html

International Rhino Foundation
Species information; conservation; membership
14000 International Road
Cumberland, OH 43732
IrhinoF@aol.com
http://www.rhinos-irf.org/

Mammal Society of Great Britain
15 Cloisters House
8 Battersea Park Road
London, SW8 4BG
Tel: (020) 7498-4358
Fax: (020) 7622-8722
enquiries@mammal.org.u.k.
www.abdn.ac.u.k./mammal/

Marine Mammal Center
Rescue and rehabilitation center for injured marine mammals; membership and adoption programs
The Marin Headlands
1065 Fort Cronkhite
Sausalito, CA 94965
Tel: (415) 289-SEAL
Fax: (415) 289-7333
http://www.tmmc.org/member.htm

Rainforest Action Network (RAN)
Rain-forest information and conservation; membership
Suite 500, 221 Pine Street
San Francisco, CA 94104
Tel: (415) 398-4404
Fax: (415) 398-2732
rainforest@ran.org
http://www.ran.org/intro.html

Tropical Savannas Cooperative Research Centre
Research and news features on Australian tropical savanna biome
Northern Territory University
Faculty of Science
Darwin, NT 0909
Australia
Tel: (08) 8946-6834
Fax: (08) 8946-7107
http://savanna.ntu.edu.au/index.html

MUSEUMS AND ZOOS

Lincoln Park Zoo
Species profiles; membership; animal adoption programs
2001 North Clark Street
Chicago, IL 60614
Tel: (312) 742-2000
http://www.lpzoo.com/animals/mammals/mammalist.html

National Museum of Natural History, Smithsonian Institution
10th Street and Constitution Avenue NW
Washington, DC 20560-0105
Tel: (202) 357-2078
webmaster@www.nmnh.si.eu
http://www.nmnh.si.edu/vert/mammals/mammals.html

San Diego Zoo
Operated by the Zoological Society of San Diego, which also runs the Wild Animal Park and the Center for Reproduction of Endangered Species
P.O. Box 551
San Diego, CA 92112-0551
Tel: (619) 231-1515 (zoo)
Tel: (760) 747-8702 (park)
http://www.sandiegozoo.org/

NATIONAL PARKS

Bako National Park, Malaysia
Coastal forests and stone formations; rare proboscis and silver-leaf monkeys; long-tailed macaques
Sarawak Tourism Centre
Tel: 082-240620
Fax: 082-427151
http://www.visitmalaysia.com/bako.html

Corcovado National Park, Costa Rica
Two hundred and ten square miles of
tropical rain forest; more than 139
mammal species
http://www.centralamerica.com/cr/parks/
#corcovado

Exmoor National Park, England
Coastal Devon and Somerset
Moors and wooded valleys; deer
and wild ponies
Exmoor National Park Visitor Centre
The Esplanade
Lynmouth
Devon, United Kingdom
Tel: 01598-752509
http://www.apgate.com/exmoor/
index.htm

Fiordland National Park,
New Zealand
One of largest wilderness sites in
world, more than 4,833 square miles;
access strictly controlled because of
rare indigenous flora and fauna
Fiordland Promotions
P.O. Box 155
Te Anau, New Zealand
fpai@xtra.co.nz
www.fiordland.org.nz

Gates of the Arctic National
Park and Preserve, Alaska
Boreal forest and arctic tundra inhabited
by caribou, dall sheep, wolves, and bears
Gates of the Arctic National Park &
Preserve / Yukon-Charley Rivers National
Preserve
Fairbanks Office (Headquarters)
Doyon Building, 201 First Avenue
Fairbanks, AK 99701
Tel: (907) 456-0281
http://www.nps.gov/gaar/

Great Smoky Mountains
National Park, Tennessee
Eight hundred square miles of temperate
forest; large variety of flora and fauna
107 Park Headquarters Road
Gatlinburg, TN 37738
Tel: (423) 436-1200
http://www.nps.gov/grsm/

Kalahari Gemsbok National Park,
South Africa
Region of large mammal migrations;
gemsbok, eland, and blue wildebeest
South African Tourist Bureau
U.S. address:
Suite 2040, 500 Fifth Avenue
20th Floor
New York, NY 10110
Tel: (212) 730-2929
Tel: (800) 822-5368
Fax: (212) 764-1980
http://www.southafrica.net/tourism/
U.K. address:
No. 5 & 6 Alt Grove
Wimbledon SW19 4DZ
Tel: (181) 944-8080
Fax: (181) 944-6705

Jasper National Park, Canada
Part of UNESCO World Heritage site;
habitat for many alpine mammal species
P.O. Box 10
Jasper, Alberta
Canada T0E 1E0
Tel: (780) 852-6176
Fax: (780) 852-5601
http://www.worldweb.com/
ParksCanada-Jasper/

Lake District National Park,
England
The largest of England's national parks;
mountains and moors
Lake District National Park Authority
Murley Moss, Oxenholme Road
Kendal, Cumbria
United Kingdom LA9 7RL
Tel: 01539-724555
Fax: 01539-740822
http://www.lake-district.gov.u.k./

Nam Bai Cat Tien National Park,
Viet Nam
Proposed as a biosphere reserve under
UNESCO; home of the extremely endangered Javan Rhinoceros
http://www.wcmc.org.u.k./infoserv/
countryp/vietnam/app7.html

Otway National Park, Australia
Coastal habitat for many rare Australian
mammal species
Australian Tourist Commission
324 Saint Kilda Road
Melbourne, Victoria 3004
Australia
Tel: (03) 690-3900
http://www.gorp.com/gorp/location/
australi/otway.htm

Ranthambore National Park, India
One of largest tiger sanctuaries in world
Ranthambore National Park
Sawai Madhopur
Rajasthan, India
http://travel.indiamart.com/places/
sanctury/ranthambhor.html

Sarek National Park, Sweden
Large alpine tundra biome
Turism i Jokkmokk
Box 124, Stortorget 4
SE-962 23 Jokkmokk
Sweden
Tel: +46-971-121-40
natur@environ.se
http://www.environ.se:8084/documents/
nature/engpark/enpstart.htm

Serengeti National Park, Tanzania
More than 14, 700 square miles of
grasslands; habitat for some three
million large mammals
http://www.tanzania-
web.com/parks/serenget.htm

Yellowstone National Park, U.S.
Thirty-four hundred square miles of
plateaus, forests, and meadows; home
to one of continent's biggest and most
varied large mammal populations
P.O. Box 168
Yellowstone, WY 82190-0168
Tel: (307) 344-7381
http://www.nps.gov/yell/

Yosemite National Park, U.S.
Twelve hundred square-mile portion
of central Sierra Nevada
P.O. Box 577
Yosemite, CA 95389
Tel: (209) 372-0200
http://www.nps.gov/yose/

Yugud-Va National Park, Russia
More than forty-six hundred square
miles of Ural mountain range; home
to bear, deer, and arctic fox
169700 Komi Republic
Pechora 98
Pechorskiy branch of N.P. Yugud-Va
Tel: (821-42) 52507, 50836, 51605, 24449
http://www.sll.fi/mpe/yugudva/intro.html

ECOTOURS

American Museum of Natural History Discovery Tours
Custom-designed expeditions
throughout world
Central Park West at 79th Street
New York, NY 10024
Tel: 1-800-462-8687
http://www.amnh.org/welcome/
discotours/

Oceanic Society Expeditions
Research expeditions and
whale-watching
Building E, Ft Mason Center
San Francisco, CA 94123
Tel: (415) 441-1106
Tel: 1-800-326-7491
Fax: (415) 474-3395
http://www.oceanic-society.org/ose.htm

Sierra Club
Outing Department
Second Floor, 85 Second Street
San Francisco, CA 94105-3441
Tel: (415) 977-5630
national.outings@sierraclub.org
http://www.sierraclub.org/outings/

PARK DIRECTORIES

Great Outdoor Recreation Pages
Catalog of natural sites of interest
around world
http://www.gorp.com/

National Parks Worldwide
World directory of parks and
nature reserves
http://parksoftheworld.org/

Parks Canada
25 Eddy Street
Hull, Quebec
Canada K1A 0M5
Tel: 1-888-773-8888
parks_webmaster@pch.gc.ca
http://www.parkscanada.gc.ca/reach/
reach_e.htm

U.S. National Parks Service
http://www.nps.gov/
Complete information on national parks
throughout the United States, including
maps and tour reservation opportunities

Mammal Orders

The following list contains the numbers of known species in each living mammalian order, along with some common names for selected species. It is based on *Mammalogy* by T.A.Vaughan, J.R. Ryan, and N.J. Czaplewski (4th edition, 2000, Saunders College Publishers, Orlando). For more information on mammal classification and summaries of group characteristics, see pages 14 to 29.

SUBCLASS PROTOTHERIA
Order Monotremata (3 species)
echidnas, duck-billed platypus

SUBCLASS THERIA
Infraclass Metatheria (Marsupialia)
Order Didelphimorphia (63 species)
opossums

Order Paucituberculata (6 species)
rat opossums

Order Microbiotheria (1 species)
monito del monte (or llaca)

Order Dasyuromorphia (63 species)
numbat, quolls, antechinuses, devil

Order Peramelemorphia (21 species)
bandicoots

Order Notoryctemorphia (2 species)
marsupial "mole"

Order Diprotodontia (117 species)
koala, wombats, cuscuses, rat kangaroos, kangaroos, wallabies, gliders, possums

Infraclass Eutheria (Placentalia)
Order Xenarthra (29 species)
two and three-toed sloths, armadillos, anteaters

Order Insectivora (429 species)
solenodons, tenrecs, hedgehogs, shrews, moles

Order Scandentia (19 species)
tree shrews

Order Dermoptera (2 species)
colugos

Order Chiroptera (928 species)
bats

Order Primates (236 species)
aye-aye, lemurs, tarsiers, monkeys, apes, human, gibbons, marmosets

Order Carnivora (271 species)
cats, civets, mongooses, hyenas, wolves, foxes, jackals, bears, seals, sea lions, walrus, weasels, skunks, otters, raccoons

Order Cetacea (78 species)
rorquals, whales, dolphins, porpoises, narwhal, beluga

Order Sirenia (5 species)
dugongs (or sea cows), manatees

Order Proboscidea (2 species)
elephants

Order Perissodactyla (18 species)
horses, asses, zebras, tapirs, rhinoceroses

Order Hyracoidea (6 species)
hyraxes

Order Tubulidentata (1 species)
aardvark

Order Artiodactyla (220 species)
swine, peccaries, hippopotamuses, camels, llamas, chevrotains, giraffe, okapi, deer, pronghorns, antelope, bison, cattle, goats

Order Pholidota (7 species)
pangolins (or scaly anteaters)

Order Rodentia (2,024 species)
squirrels, beavers, pocket gophers, rats, mice, kangaroo, rats, dormice, Old and New World porcupines, cavies, mole-rats, chinchillas, capybara, pacas, agoutis

Order Lagomorpha (80 species)
pikas, rabbits

Order Macroscelidea (15 species)
elephant-shrews

Orders at Risk

The following list of mammal orders and number of critically endangered (CR) and endangered (EN) species is taken from the 1996 *World Monitoring Centre's Red List of Threatened Animals.* Orders Paucituberculata, Microbiotheria, Dermoptera, Hyracoidea, Tubulidentata, Pholidota, and Sirenia have no mammal species on the critically endangered list or the endangered list—and so are not included below. For the complete Red List of 681 mammalian species and sub-species, contact the World Monitoring Centre:

e-mail: info@wcmc.org.uk
website: http://www.wcmc.org.uk/

SUBCLASS PROTOTHERIA

Order Monotremata
CR 0 species; EN 1 species: long-nosed echidna

SUBCLASS THERIA

Infraclass Metatheria (Marsupialia)

Order Didelphimorphia
CR 3 species: e.g. Handley's mouse opossum ; EN 3 species: e.g. *Marmosa xerophila*

Order Dasyuromorphia
CR 1 species: *Sminthopsis griseoventer;* EN 9 species: e.g. Leadbeater's possum

Order Peramelemorphia
CR 2 species: e.g. eastern-barred bandicoot; EN 1 species: long-nosed bandicoot

Order Notoryctemorphia
CR 0 species; EN 2 species: northern marsupial mole, southern marsupial mole

Order Diprotodontia
CR 3 species: e.g. Gilbert's potoroo, northern hairy-nosed wombat; EN 12 species: e.g. Goodfellow's tree kangaroo

Infraclass Eutheria (Placentalia)

Order Xenarthra
CR 0 species; EN 3 species: maned sloth, pink fairy armadillo, giant armadillo

Order Insectivora
CR 37 species: e.g. Juliana's golden mole, Malayan water shrew; EN 48 species: e.g. Haitian solenodon, giant golden mole, Mindanao moonrat

Order Scandentia
CR 0 species; EN 2 species: e.g. Bornean tree shrew

Order Chiroptera
CR 26 species: e.g. Rodriguez' flying fox; EN 32 species: e.g. Kitti's hog-nosed bat

Order Primates
CR 14 species: e.g. mountain gorilla, Javan gibbon; EN 29 species: e.g. indri, chimpanzee, bonobo, gibbon

Order Carnivora
CR 5 species: e.g. red wolf, Mediterranean monk seal; EN 25 species: e.g. tiger, African hunting dog, snow leopard

Order Cetacea
CR 2 species: Chinese lake dolphin, gulf porpoise; EN 10 species: e.g. blue whale, gray whale, bowhead whale

Order Proboscidea
CR 0 species; EN 2 species: African elephant, Asian elephant

Order Perissodactyla
CR 4 species: e.g. Javan rhinoceros, black rhinoceros; EN 4 species: e.g. mountain zebra, great Indian rhinoceros

Order Artiodactyla
CR 9 species: e.g. Przewalski's gazelle; EN 28 species: e.g. bactrian camel, Saola

Order Rodentia
CR 66 species: e.g. Mount Graham red squirrel; EN 97 species: e.g. Idaho ground squirrel, Japanese dormouse

Order Lagomorpha
CR 3 species: e.g. Helan Shan pika; EN 8 species: e.g. riverine rabbit, Ryukyu rabbit

Order Macroscelidea
CR 0 species; EN 3 species: e.g. golden-rumped elephant-shrew

Glossary

Altricial: Offspring born in a helpless state, with extreme dependence on parent—e.g. newborn marsupials, rodents. See *Precocial*.

Altruistic behavior: Behavior favoring well-being of another individual. See *Kin selection*.

Apnea: The temporary cessation of breathing.

Arboreal: Living mainly within trees.

Biome: Biogeographical region defined by a series of interrelated and characteristic life forms—e.g. tundra, taiga, rain forest.

Bulla: Bony compartment within the mammalian skull housing the middle and inner ear.

Coevolution: When two different species reciprocally influence each other's adaptation.

Convergence/convergent evolution: The evolving of similar characteristics in different species through adaptation to similar functions or environments. See *Parallelism*.

Crepuscular: Active at dawn and dusk.

Delayed fertilization: A situation where sperm deposited in the female's reproductive tract stays viable for up to several months until ovulation and fertilization occur.

Delayed implantation: Delayed development of fertilized ovum, retained in uterus in a dormant state for up to several months.

Digitigrade: A foot posture in which the "heel" is off the ground and weight of the body is supported by the balls of the feet—e.g. the way cats and dogs walk.

Diurnal: Active mainly during daylight hours.

Echolocation: A sensory system involving the emission of sounds and use of returning echoes to sense surroundings; used by many bats and some insectivores and cetaceans to navigate and search for prey.

Ectotherm: An animal in which body temperature is determined by that of the environment—e.g. reptiles and amphibians.

Endotherm: An animal in which body temperature is maintained constant, independent of the surrounding environment—e.g. mammals and birds.

Estrus: Also called "heat" in domesticated mammals, this is the period when female mammals permit copulation.

Family: A taxonomic subdivision of an order, suborder, or superfamily; it contains a group of related subfamilies, tribes, and genera. Animal families always end in "idae"—e.g. family Phyllostomidae.

Genus (plur. genera): A taxonomic division between family and species; a grouping of one or more species believed to be of a single evolutionary origin—e.g. genus *Microtus*.

Gestation: The period of development of the embryo from fertilization to birth within the mother's body.

Harem: A group of females guarded by a single male that prevents other males from mating with members of the group.

Hibernation: Energy-saving period of inactivity in which body temperature and metabolic rate drop in response to cold ambient temperatures.

Home range: The territory in which an individual or group spends most of its time.

Induced ovulation: The release of an egg triggered by the act of copulation.

Kin selection: Natural selection that affects the survival and reproductive success of genetically related individuals.

Life zone: See *Biome*.

Marsupium: External pouch in the abdominal wall enclosing the mammary glands that serves to incubate the young of most marsupials and some monotremes.

Nocturnal: Active mainly at night.

Parallelism/parallel evolution: Similar evolutionary adaptations found in two or more related species such that the same features undergo similar changes—e.g. the different types of elongated snouts developed by different species of nectar-feeding bats. See *Convergence*.

Pelage: All the hair or fur on a mammal.

Pheromones: Odorous chemical compounds used in communication between members of the same species.

Plantigrade: A foot posture in which the entire base of the foot rests on the ground—e.g. the way primates walk.

Precocial: Refers to young that are born relatively well-developed, requiring minimal parental care—e.g. new-born ungulates.

Prehensile: Anatomical structures that are capable of grasping by wrapping around an object such as a food item or a tree branch—e.g. tails, noses, thumbs, lips.

Proboscis: An elongated, varyingly flexible snout—e.g. as with elephants, tapirs, proboscis monkeys.

Reciprocal altruism: The trading back and forth of resources or altruistic actions by two or more individuals.

Ruminant: A mammal in which the digestive process includes the regurgitation and rechewing of plant food to improve its digestibility by microbes—e.g. cows, goats, sheep.

Rut: Refers to the alert state of the male during mating ("rutting") season.

Sperm competition: Competition between males at the level of fertilization, where the sperm from one mating competes with other sperm to fertilize the egg; usually involves multimated (so-called promiscuous) females.

Species: Group of individuals having common characteristics and the capability of breeding with each other and producing fertile offspring; members of the same species share similar appearance, behavior, and common evolutionary history—e.g. species *Microtus californicus*.

Taxonomy: The scientific classification and naming system used for animals and plants.

Torpor: A type of adaptive hypothermia or dormancy in which body temperature, heart rate, and respiration are reduced; generally briefer and shallower than hibernation.

Unguligrade: Type of foot posture found in ungulates, in which only the hoofs or toenails touch the ground.

Vibrissae: Long, stiff hairs usually found on the mammal snout that act as sensory receptors.

Index

otter(s)
    giant, 112*
    sea, 12, *34*, 77, 81
otters, 22, 77
oval window, 48
ovaries, 40, *40*
Ovibos maschatus, 168*
Ovis canadensis, 75
Ovis dalli, 92*
ovulation, 40
    induced, 183
oxytocin, 57
Ozotoceros bezoarticus, 124*

P

paca, 116*
pacarana, 28
pacas, 28
packrat, 94
Pan troglodytes, 21
panda, giant, 22, 32, 81, 153*
pangolin
    cape, *27*
    tree, 115*
pangolins, 27, 39
Panthera leo, 121*
Panthera onca, 112*
Pantholops hodgsoni, 135*
panting, 12
Papio cynocephalus, 61
Papio hamadryas, 60
parallel evolution, 183
parks, national, 177-179
Paucituberculata, 16, 180, 181
peccaries, 25, 26
pelage, 183
    See also hair
pelvis, *8*
penis, 40
Peramelemorphia, 16, 180, 181
Perissodactyla, 25, *82*, 180, 181
Peromyscus eremicus, 140*
Peromyscus leucopus, 158*
Peromyscus maniculatus, 158
Petaurus breviceps, 60, 99*
Phacochoerus aethiopicus, 138*
phalangers, 16
Phalangista maculata, 97*
Phascolarctus cinereus, 16, *16*
pheromones, 51, 52, 183
Phoca groenlandica, 171*
Phoca vitulina, 81
Phocoena phocoena, 172*
Pholidota, 27, *83*, 180
Physeter catodon, 173*
pichi, 120*
pig
    bush, 114
    red river, 114
pigs, 26
    bicornuate uterus, *40*
    scent glands, 52

pika
    American, 95*
    Helan Shan, 181
pikas, 29
piloerection, 47
pinnae, 48, *48*, *49*
pinnipeds, delayed
        implantation in, 42
pituitary gland, 44
placenta, 41
placental mammals, 14, 17-29
Placentalia (infraclass
        Eutheria), 180, 181
plague, 70
plantigrade posture, 74, *74*,
        183
    See also walking
platypus, duck-billed, *15*, 97*
    courtship, 64-65
    eggs, 43
    internal scrotum, 41
    ovaries, *40*
    poison glands, 15, *34*, 97
play, 58-59, *58-59*
pocket gopher, plains, 148*
pocket gophers, 28
pocket mice, 28
polecat, steppe, 144*
porcupine(s)
    crested, 39, 141*
    North American, *74*,
        76, 164*
    prehensile-tailed, 117*
porcupines, 28
    protective behavior, 39
    quills, 13
    tracks, *74*
porpoise
    gulf, 181
    harbor, 172*
porpoises, 23, 45
possum
    Leadbeater's, 99*
    striped, 16, 100*
    See also opossum
possums, 16
Potamochoerus porcus, 114*
Potamogale velox, 102*
potoroo, Gilbert's, 181
Potos flavus, 111*
prairie dog, black-tailed, 147*
precocial young, 42, 183
predatory behavior, 32-33,
        38-39
prehensile, 183
primates, 21
    Old World, 40-41
    simplex uterus, *40*
Primates (order), *83*, 180, 181
Proboscidea, 24, *82*, 180, 181
proboscis, 24, 183
Procavia capensis, 123*

Procyon lotor, *74*, 154*
pronghorn, 146*
    Sonoran, 181
pronghorns, 25
Proteles cristatus, 22
Protheria, 14, 15, 180, 181
Pseudois nayaur, 92*
Pseudoryx nghetinhensis, 96
Pteronura brasiliensis, 112*
Ptilocercus lowii, 19
puberty, 40
pudu, southern, 155*
Pudu pudu, 155*

Q-R

quills, 13
quokka, 131*
quoll
    spotted-tail, 181
    tiger, 59
quolls, 16
rabbit
    European, 61, 159*
    red-rumped, 96, *96*
    riverine, 181
    Ryukyu, 181
rabbits, 29, 72
raccoon, 71, *74*, 154*
raccoon dog, 152*
raccoons, 22
    pinned back ears, 47
    tapetum, 47
    tracks, *74*
    trail, *75*
rainfall in biomes, 84-85
Rangifer tarandus, 75, 79,
        168*
rat
    black, 53, 70
    brown, 70
rat kangaroo, brush-tailed,
        130*
rat kangaroos, 16
rats, 28
    brain, *45*, *53*
    vision, 46
    whiskers, 53
Rattus norvegicus, 70
Rattus rattus, 53, 70
ratunculus, 53
reciprocal altruism, 62-63, 183
Reithrodontomys megalotis, 43
reproduction, *40*, 40-43, *41*
    courtship, 64-65
    delayed development,
        41-42
    delayed fertilization, 41,
        81, 182
    delayed implantation, 42,
        182
    induced ovulation, 183
    mating, 64-65, *64-65*

Tasmanian devil, 16, 98*
taste, sense of, 45, 52, 52-53
taxonomy, 14, 183
teeth, 8, 33
    adaptations for food types, 32-33
    carnassials, 32, 33
    evolution of, 31
    of lagomorphs, 29
    lophodont molars, 33
    in predatory behavior, 38-39
    of rodents, 28
temperate forest biome, 84-85, 150, 150, 151-159
temperate grassland biome, 84-85, 142, 142, 143-149
temperature in biomes, 84-85
tenrec, aquatic, 18
tenrecs, 13, 18, 45
territorial behavior, 60-61
    marking, 51, 51-52
testes, 41
testosterone, 41
tetrapoda, 34
therapsids, 30
Theria, 14, 15, 180, 181
Theropithecus gelada, 120*
thumbs, opposable, 35
thylacine, 16
tigers, 13, 181
torpor, 11, 12, 183
touch, sense of, 45, 53, 53
tracking mammals, 72-73, 72 75, 74-75
Tragulus meminna, 115*
trails, 72, 75
tree kangaroo
    Goodfellow's, 98*
    Scott's, 181
tree shrew
    Bornean, 181
    common, 19, 103*
    feather-tailed, 19
tree shrews, 19
Trichechus manatus, 174*
tropical forest biome, 84-85, 96, 96, 97-117
tropical grassland and savanna biome, 84-85, 118, 118, 119-127
Tubulidentata, 27, 83, 180
tuco-tucos, 28
tundra biome, 84-85, 166, 166, 167-169
Tupaia glis, 19, 103*
turbinates, 50
Tursiops truncatus, 23
tusks, 39

U-V
uakari
    bald, 110*
    red, 110
Uncia uncia, 89*
ungulates, 25-26
unguligrade posture, 75, 183
    See also walking
urban dwellers, 70-71, 70-71
urine to mark territory, 51, 52
URLs, 176-179, 181
Urocyon cinereoargenteus, 150
Uroderma bilobatus, 105*
Ursus americanus, 74, 152*
Ursus arctos, 79
Ursus maritimus, 167*
Ursus thibetanus, 22
uterus, 8, 40, 40
vagina, 40, 40
Vampyrum spectrum, 105*
vasopressin, 57
venom in saliva, 18
vibrissae, 13, 53, 53, 183
Vicugna vicugna, 87, 144*
vicuña, 144*
    Andean, 87
viscacha, 142
viscachas, 28
vision, 45, 46-47
vocalizations, 49
vole
    meadow, 78, 86
    northern red-backed, 165*
    polar red-backed, 165
    sagebrush, 149*
    squirrel mouse, 165
    taiga, 165
    woodland, 159*
    yellow-cheeked, 165*
vomeronasal organ, 52
Vulpes velox, 134*
Vulpes vulpes, 74, 153*
Vulpes zerda, 48, 133*

W-X-Y-Z
Walker, Stephen, 55
walking, 34-35
wallabies, 16
wallaby, Tammar, 42
walrus, 22, 170*
walruses
    locomotion, 35
    mating behavior, 64
    tusk use, 39
wapiti, 155*
    marking, 52
    mating behavior, 64
    rutting, 77
    tracks, 75
    See also Cervus elaphus
warm-bloodedness, 10-11
warthog, desert, 138*

Washoe, 55
watching mammals, 68-79
weasel, least, 46
weasels, 22, 38
weight, 8
whale(s)
    baleen (mysticeti), 23, 50
    blue, 8, 23, 43, 174*, 181
    bowhead, 181
    gray, 23, 63, 80
    great sperm, 173*
    humpback, 64, 76
    killer, 81
    minke, 23
    northern right, 173*
    right, 23, 43
    toothed (odontoceti), 23, 50
whale watching, 69, 69
whales, 23
    echolocation, 45
    locomotion, 35
    migration, 11, 80
    singing, 64
    vibrissae, 13
whiskers, 53, 53
wildebeest (blue gnu), 57, 125, 125*
Wilson, E.O., 80
winter survival, 77-79
wolf
    gray, 38, 51, 74, 163*
    maned, 142
    red, 181
    Tasmanian (extinct), 37
wolverine tracks, 74
wolves, 22
    teeth, 32
    tracks, 74
    trail, 75
wombat
    northern hairy-nosed, 181
    southern hairy-nosed, 119*
wombats, 16
woodchuck (groundhog), 49, 78
woodrat, bushy-tailed, 94*
woylie, 130
Xenarthra, 17, 82, 180
xenarthrans, 17
yak, 90*
yapok, 16
young, care of, 42-43, 42-43
Zaedyus pichiy, 120*
Zaglossus bruijni, 15, 15
Zapus hudsonius, 149*
zebra
    common, 42, 123*
    mountain, 181
zebras, 25
zoos, 177

ST. REMY MEDIA

President: Pierre Léveillé
Vice-President, Finance: Natalie Watanabe
Managing Editor: Carolyn Jackson
Managing Art Director: Diane Denoncourt
Production Manager: Michelle Turbide
Director, Business Development: Christopher Jackson
Senior Editor: Elizabeth Lewis
Art Director: Solange Laberge
Assistant Editor: Robert Labelle
Writers: Stacey Berman, Angela Cone, Jim Hynes,
    Alan Morantz, Fiona Reid, Jeff Rosenfeld,
    Daniel Schneider, Andrew Walde
Researcher: Jessica Braun, Heather Mills
Illustrators: Monique Chaussé, Patrick Jougla,
    Rosemarie Schwab
Photo Researcher: Linda Castle
Indexer: Linda Cardella Cournoyer
Senior Editor, Production: Brian Parsons
Systems Director: Edward Renaud
Technical Support: Joey Fraser, Jean Sirois
Scanner Operator: Martin Francoeur

The following persons also assisted in the preparation of this book:
Lorraine Doré, Dominique Gagné, Pascale Hueber, and
Rob Lutes.

ACKNOWLEDGMENTS
The editors wish to thank the following:
Catherine Badgley, University of Michigan; Dominique
Bertaux, McGill University; George Constable; Suzanne
MacDonald, York University; Steve Manning, Discovery
Channel.